Why Do Chemical Reactions Occur?

Why

Do Chemical Reactions

Occur?

J. Arthur Campbell

Harvey Mudd College

PRENTICE-HALL, INC., Englewood Cliffs, N. J.

To Kirsten and her generation

FOUNDATIONS OF MODERN CHEMISTRY SERIES

Robert W. Parry and Henry Taube, Editors

This monograph is designed as an extension of CHEM Study materials

Current printing (last digit):
12   11   10   9   8   7   6   5   4

C 95871 P
C 95872 C

Preface

Most of the main concepts of science in general, and chemistry in particular, are at least introduced in the general courses taught at the first-year college level, or even at the high-school level. But one idea, of major importance, which has gone almost unmentioned in the past, is the importance of random ness, or *entropy*, in determining the nature of changes and whether they will occur.

Usually approached through the cold logic of a heat engine, entropy more often frightens than enlightens students. Nor is the relationship between adiabatics, isothermals, and chemical reactions obvious.

Most scientific concepts are first brought to the attention of students in a semi-quantitative, even intuitive way. They grow up with the concept of energy. The concepts of evolution are becoming part of the working language of society. The notions of dynamic equilibria are pervading our conversation. Yet the concept of increasing entropy in all natural processes is certainly used by less than one per cent of even the literate people in the world.

I have tried here to intertwine energetics and randomness so that even a high-school student, with some experience with the new curricula in

v

chemistry and physics, will be able to appreciate their use more fully.

The monograph is designed as an extension of the Chemical Education Material (CHEM Study) course. It should be useful as supplementary reading in such a course or as a part of a subsequent first-year college course in chemistry. Both the scientific and mathematical level are selected with the non-science oriented student in mind. The approach here should provide a good background for the more mathematical and scientifically complete treatments available in other monographs in this series.

I wish to thank Harvey Mudd College for the sabbatical leave and the Guggenheim Foundation for the fellowship which provided the time, and Professor Osamu Hayaishi and his colleagues at Kyoto University who provided the pleasant surroundings that made this possible.

Much of this material is based on a paper prepared for the Organization for Economic Cooperation and Development at a meeting in Frascati, Italy, December 1961. Real appreciation is felt for the contributions of my colleagues at that meeting. I should also like publicly to thank my wife for foregoing the pleasure of visiting numerous delightful festivals and scenic spots in Japan in order that these words might be written.

J. Arthur Campbell

Claremont, California

Contents

vii

Why Do Chemical Reactions Occur?

1

Reaction and Change

The earliest record of the idea that matter is composed of atoms came from the Greeks over 2000 years ago. Today this idea is so widely accepted as to be treated as a fact upon which is based almost every discussion of science. For example, all substances are said to be made of atoms which attract and repel one another. And we believe that the forces acting between the atoms lead to the formation of chemical bonds, which hold the atoms together.

If we think of a chemical reaction as any change which forms or breaks bonds between atoms, then almost all the changes we observe involve chemical reactions. Of course, a few kinds of reactions—such as those leading to the emission of light by neon signs, by ordinary light bulbs, or by stars—may involve only changes within atoms, not the forming or breaking of bonds between atoms. Similarly, some radioactive changes may involve only changes within single atoms. But if we leave out of consideration these processes involving only single atoms we are left with the great majority of changes as chemical changes.

1

The printing of this book, the manufacture of its paper, the physiological changes in you while you read it or hold it, the flames or decay which will eventually consume it: all involve chemical changes. Man has observed such changes for tens of thousands of years. He has learned to control them, partly to his benefit and partly to his harm. Such control was originally based on empirical rules which "worked," but which appeared unrelated to one another. But with the advent of the experimental approach to the study of nature, more and more evidence accumulated that the changes could be understood in terms of a rather small number of regularities, rules, or ideas. The idea of atoms is an important case in point. Another is the idea that chemical bonds exist between the atoms. And a third is the idea that changes are due to the making and breaking of these bonds.

The idea that atoms are held together by chemical bonds which can change accounts readily for the existence of change. But it does not allow us to understand why certain changes occur and others do not. Nor does it allow us to control the conditions which may regulate the changes, nor to interpret why any particular reactions actually do occur.

Repeated observations show that wood burns in the atmosphere and glass does not. Iron rusts and gold does not. Sugar can be digested by humans and sawdust cannot. Chlorine combines vigorously with hot tungsten; nitrogen and neon do not.

As a result of this last observation, most tungsten-filament light bulbs contain some gaseous nitrogen or neon, but no chlorine. For whereas the first two gases increase the lifetime of the bulb, chlorine would greatly decrease it. We do not need to know, in order to construct the light bulb, why these substances behave differently, but many people find the pursuit of such knowledge exciting. And an even larger number of people enjoy the new products that always have followed the discovery of some generalization or idea which ties together and "explains" previously incomprehensible observations. For example, since we understand a great deal about the reactions involved, we now know how to minimize the chances that wood will burn or that iron will rust. We know how to convert sawdust into digestible food, and we know why certain gases do and certain others do not react with hot tungsten. All of these discoveries enhance our ability to understand and to control the world around us. Coupled with many other observations, they provide insight into why chemical reactions occur.

The question of why reactions occur is not readily answered through observation of the reactions. The iron exterior of a blast furnace is rusting, while at the same time, inside the furnace, iron rust is being converted back into metallic iron, both reactions occurring within a few centimeters of each other, but in opposite directions. Why sometimes one and sometimes the other? At one spot in a forest a tree rots in the presence of oxygen to form carbon dioxide and water, while in another spot the water and carbon dioxide just released by the rotting tree react to form new wood and oxygen. The rotting of one tree and the growth of the other are certainly both occurring. Rotting and growth can even both occur in a single tree. The surrounding conditions are similar, yet the two chemical reactions are the reverse of one another. How is it that both can occur in nature?

Conservation Laws

Most of the great discoveries of science occurred since the time men began to make quantitative measurements concerning natural phenomena. One of the earliest such measurements in chemistry concerned the comparative masses of the reactants and the products of a reaction. Such experiments have been done many times and have confirmed repeatedly that there is no observable change in mass during a chemical reaction. Some results typical of careful experimentation are shown in Table 1.1. (They were obtained by E. W. Morley near the end of the 19th century.)

Table 1.1   WEIGHTS * OF HYDROGEN GAS AND OXYGEN GAS
REACTING TO GIVE A MEASURED WEIGHT OF WATER:
HYDROGEN PLUS OXYGEN GIVES WATER

I	II	III	IV	V
		Weight		
Weight	*Weight*	*of Hydrogen*	*Weight*	*Difference*
of	*of*	*Plus Oxygen*	*of*	*in Weight*
Hydrogen	*Oxygen*	(I + II)	*Water*	(III − IV)
3.2559	25.8531	29.1090	29.1052	+0.0038
3.8382	30.4700	34.3082	34.3151	−0.0071
3.8523	30.5818	34.4341	34.4327	+0.0014
3.8211	30.3429	34.1640	34.1559	+0.0081

* Weights in grams.

Within the inherent error of the measurements, ±0.008 g or about 2 parts in 10,000 or 0.02 per cent, we see that no mass change has occurred.

The constancy of mass, noted in millions of careful analytical experiments, is summarized in the idea that mass is always conserved; it never changes. But if mass is conserved in every chemical reaction, no study of the mass involved can give guidance as to which reactions will occur and which will not. Nor can a study of the unchanging mass tell us whether a reaction will proceed in one direction or the other.

There are many conservation "laws" known. Not only is mass conserved. So also are electrical charge, number of atoms, angular momentum, total momentum, energy, and various other quantities. But since all these quantities remain unchanged during a reaction, their study alone can never give the kind of understanding we need.

We might say that chemical reactions occur despite the fact that mass, electrical charge, energy, the number of atoms, etc., remain unchanged.

(Very accurate measurements show that many of these conservation laws are not rigorously followed by actual systems. It is now well established that neither mass nor energy is conserved during a change. Rather, a quantity dependent on both, a quantity known as mass-energy, is now thought to be conserved. However, for our purposes the "failures" do not alter the fact that change, and direction of change, cannot be explained in terms of quantities which themselves are unaltered during the change. Conserved quantities cannot account for change, but they do limit the kind of changes that can occur.)

Although conserved quantities, such as energy, cannot account for change, we shall find it very important to consider the energy associated with a chemical reaction. The energy of the total system is unaltered but the distribution of the energy may change. And the change in distribution of the energy provides some excellent insights into the forces acting during the reaction. For example, careful measurement shows that mixing a hot substance with a cold one leads to no change in the total energy of the system. But we notice that the hot substance always cools and the cold substance always heats until both are finally at the same temperature. Thus the distribution of the energy has changed. In fact, the same type of change in energy distribution always occurs when hot and cold objects are placed together, and we use this generalization to predict the direction such a "reaction" will take. We say the change occurs "because heat always flows from a hot to a cold object." Unfortunately, we seldom adequately explore what the phrase "heat flows" means.

Similarly, even though atoms are always conserved in a chemical reaction, it proves enlightening to keep track of them. Like the energy, the atoms redistribute themselves. The change in distribution is important even though no change in the number of atoms occurs.

Thus quantities which are conserved cannot of themselves inform us as to change or the direction of change. But the redistribution of these quantities can be, and often is, of prime importance in understanding change.

The question then is why do these redistributions occur? What is it that changes, and how can reactions occur and still obey the conservation laws?

Mechanism and Extent of Reaction

Simplification of the question as to why reactions occur follows if we consider two aspects of the changes: (1) the mechanism by which the changes occur, and (2) the extent to which the changes occur.

The mechanism of the reaction refers to the step or series of steps by which the initial reactants interact in the process of forming the products. For example, the mechanism of bowling is to go to a bowling alley, select a ball, and roll it toward the pins so that it will strike the pins and make them fall, etc. The over-all, or net, effect of achieving a strike is accomplished through a complicated mechanism or series of steps.

Each step in a mechanism requires the successful completion of all prior steps before it can occur, and the over-all, or net, effect is the sum of the effects of each of the steps. Each step is itself a reaction less complicated than the over-all, or net, reaction. Thus each step in a mechanism, if the steps can be discovered, is ordinarily easier to understand than the over-all net reaction. Sometimes it may prove impossible to learn the nature of each and every step. But even then a knowledge of some of the steps may considerably simplify the problem of comprehending the main features of the net reaction.

The extent of a reaction measures the degree to which the reactants change into the products. In bowling, the extent of reaction is measured by the number of pins which fall. A reaction goes to "completion" if no detectable quantity of at least one of the reactants remains at the time of the final measurement. A reaction "does not occur" if no detectable quantity of products is found. In terms of our bowling analogy, a "strike" would be a complete reaction, and a "gutter ball" no reaction at all.

The ability to detect residual reactants or new products depends, of course, on the sensitivity of the analytical tools employed. Very sensitive analytical methods may allow the detection of a tiny amount of reaction or may allow determination of the fact that a given reaction, while it has occurred to a very great extent, has not really gone to "completion." (Let us anticipate here by saying that experiments with very sensitive analytical methods and calculations, based on the best available data, lead chemists to believe that all conceivable reactions occur to some extent and that no reaction actually goes to completion. However, it is still often convenient to talk as though certain reactions do not occur, others occur to a limited extent, and others completely consume the reactants.)

One of the principal methods for discovering the mechanism of reactions is the study of chemical kinetics, that is, the study of the change of concentrations of chemicals as a function of time, temperature, and concentration of the substances. Such studies can yield data on the rate of the reaction. From the rate data, in turn, valuable information concerning the mechanism may be deduced. In some cases compounds intermediate between reactants and products can be detected giving evidence as to the substances involved in certain of the mechanistic steps.

A principal way of correlating the extent of reaction is in terms of the distribution of energy between the reactants and products. Much of this is possible through the application of chemical thermodynamics. The extent of reaction is measured by comparing the amount of products to the amount of reactants. This is done after the system has reacted a sufficient time so that no further net reaction is occurring, i.e., after the system has come to equilibrium with respect to the reaction under consideration.

There is no necessary correlation between the rate or mechanism of a reaction and its extent at equilibrium. Some reactions of very complex mechanism, such as the combustion of hydrogen and oxygen, proceed almost to completion at room temperature, but only at a very slow rate. Others, with equally complicated mechanisms, such as the digestion of glucose, proceed almost to completion at a higher rate. Still others, such as the solution of a solid in water, may occur to only a small extent even though the rate of reaction is high.

It is important to distinguish small extent of reaction, as in the solution of many solids in water, from small *apparent extent* of reaction due to a slow rate, as in the combination of hydrogen with oxygen. The hydrogen and oxygen will eventually combine almost completely, whereas only small amounts of the solids dissolve, no matter how long one waits.

We shall first consider the mechanisms and rates of reactions, and then turn to the extent of reaction, or equilibrium, considerations.

Questions

1. List the interatomic bonds which are broken or formed in the following. If your answer is "none," describe how the change occurred without changing the interatomic bonds. Qualitatively classify the bonds involved as strong or weak.
   a. Burning of carbon to give carbon dioxide
   b. Writing with a lead (graphite) pencil on paper
   c. Dissolving of sugar in water
   d. Rusting of iron
   e. Stretching a rubber band
   f. Emission of gamma rays by radioactive iron
2. Select three or four changes you observe each day and interpret them in terms of the making or breaking of bonds between atoms.
3. Conservation of atoms is an idea that is universally used by chemists (as in balancing chemical equations). Yet the number of atoms in the universe is constantly changing due to fusion and fission of atoms. How can the chemist apply the idea of atomic conservation with as great success as he does?
4. Write a description for the *net reaction* and for the *mechanistic steps* of some change. Would your answer agree with the statement, "Net reactions are easier to describe, but mechanistic steps are easier to understand"?
5. List some changes that occur slowly, but result finally in "almost complete reaction." List some which occur rapidly and quickly come to measurable equilibrium between reactants and products. Do you observe any regularities among the changes listed in each group which might allow you to describe why a particular change might fall into one or another of the two groups?

2

An Experimental

Approach

Experimental observations serve as the source of most ideas in science. So let us consider the following experiment in our attempt to discover the necessary conditions for chemical reactions to occur. A one liter flask is half filled with water, and 10 g of sodium hydroxide are dissolved in it. Ten g of dextrose (glucose) are then added and allowed to dissolve. About one ml of a 1 per cent solution of methylene blue in ethyl alcohol is then added. Upon standing in a stoppered flask, the resulting solution becomes colorless.

Superficial examination would not distinguish the quiescent solution from a pure liquid, but if we shake the solution it turns a deep blue. The blue color disappears on standing but may be restored by further shaking. This cycle of shaking a colorless solution to produce a blue one which then turns colorless on standing may be repeated many times. Why do these reactions occur?

The most effective way for the reader to explore possible answers to this question is for him to cease to be solely a reader and to become an experimental scientist. He may obtain the ingredients for the experiment at most drugstores. The experiment itself is safe, except for the possible blue stains that a sloppy experimenter will cause by spilling the ingredients. And the results of personal observation, searching for regularities, wondering about the results, and trying to write an interpretation understandable to others are considerable. Furthermore, even if he knows nothing about the chemical contents of the flask in terms of names of chemicals, formulas, or even number of chemicals present, it is possible for a neophyte to make sufficient observations to arrive at a valid conclusion concerning the general mechanism of the reactions which must be occurring.

Let us assume that we do not know the contents of the flask but can only make observations and interpret them. This approach will emphasize the importance of careful experimental observation.

Some Experimental Observations

We start with a flask containing a colorless liquid, which might very well be a pure substance, such as water, benzene, alcohol. (We can conclude that it could not, for example, be glycerine, because our liquid is not syrupy as we can see by shaking it.) When the liquid is shaken vigorously it turns blue. Why?

Perhaps there is a reaction between the liquid and the stopper. But shaking without contact between liquid and stopper also results in the blue color, and inverting the flask so that liquid and stopper come into contact without shaking does not result in blue. Nor does the increased contact with the walls of the flask cause the blue since simply swirling the contents increases this contact but does not produce a blue color.

Perhaps the energy added by stirring raises the temperature of the liquid and turns it blue. As the liquid then sits, the temperature falls to its original value and the liquid regains its colorless state. Notice that this suggestion has the considerable merit of interpreting both changes—not just the "bluing" reaction. Is it a realistic interpretation? It is based on the idea that the flask gets warmer on shaking. But the flask can be warmed in other ways than by shaking. For example, the small temperature rise due to shaking can also be accomplished merely by holding the flask in one's hands. But no change to blue occurs. Even vigorous heating does not cause a color change, nor does cooling. The idea that a temperature change was important fits some of the experimental data, but does not fit all of them. Therefore it must be discarded.

Though we have concentrated on the liquid in the flask it is possible that the sealed flask also contains a gas. When the contents are shaken the gas and liquid may mix, react, and produce the color change. This is consistent too with the fact that merely swirling the flask produces no color change, nor does simply inverting it without mixing the gas and the liquid. What further experiments can be done to check the possible role of any gas present?

One way to solve problems is to combine thinking with actions. If it is true that the blue color is caused by contact between gas and liquid what should careful observation of the unshaken flask disclose? After all, the gas and liquid are continuously in contact at their interface. If mere contact is required the interface should be blue. Now examine the quiescent flask. There is indeed a thin, sometimes very thin, blue layer at the top of the liquid. (See Figure 2.1.) Gentle tilting breaks the layer and lets streamers of it mix with the bulk liquid. The blue streamers then disappear. Our prediction has been borne out by observation, adding credence to the idea that mixing the gas and liquid produces the blue color.

Or perhaps the thin blue layer simply mixes with the rest of the liquid upon shaking, coloring the whole liquid and then rising to the top again upon standing?

Again there are various methods of checking the relative merits of the two interpretations. One is to shake the solution to produce the blue color and then to watch carefully as it disappears. If "creaming" of a blue layer occurs, the color should first disappear at the bottom of the liquid and gradually rise toward the top.

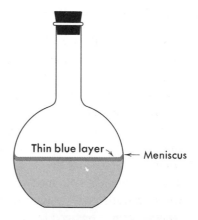

FIGURE *2.1* *The surface of the liquid is always covered by a thin blue layer, even when the rest of the liquid is colorless.*

This can sometimes be best checked, especially in a long-necked flask, by inverting the flask during the debluing reaction. The color changes uniformly throughout the liquid. Creaming of a blue layer is not observed.

All of the experimental evidence thus far has been obtained with the flask continuously sealed. Opening the flask may, of course, change the contents and alter the experimental conditions. However, if we decide to run this risk, we may replace the gas in the flask with air and again try the experiment. Bluing and debluing still occur. If we now try another gas, say natural gas since it is so readily available in many places, we find no bluing reaction occurs. All this adds further credence to the idea that shaking mixes the gas and the liquid. It also shows that not all gases are effective. But we have discovered that air, or more probably one of the components of air, is effective. Evacuation of the flask also stops the bluing reaction, further confirming the necessity of a gas similar to one of those found in air.

We can now write a preliminary "chemical equation" to summarize the bluing reaction:

$$gas + liquid \rightarrow blue$$

The reactions can occur only when the reaction partners come into contact. "Contact" on a macroscopic scale implies "collisions" on the molecular scale, because the molecules are in motion. Thus we conclude that the reaction can occur only when the reacting molecules collide, as at the surface or upon shaking, and cannot occur when the collisions become impossible, as in the bulk of the unshaken solution or in a flask containing none of the required gas. Molecular contact or collision is, thus, the first requirement to be met before a chemical reaction can occur.

But what about the debluing reaction? Is it simply a reversal of the reaction just written? That is, does the gas merely escape from the liquid upon standing and the system then revert to its original state? We have actually already settled this possibility when we investigated the possibility of "creaming" in the system. We found then that the color disappears uniformly throughout the liquid, whereas if the color change were due to gas escaping from the solution, the color would disappear first at the bottom of the flask, then more or less slowly toward the top as the rising gas finally escaped from the solution there.

(It is also axiomatic in chemistry—although we will only state rather than prove it here—that reactions cannot reverse completely without some change in conditions. It is true that bubbles of a gas and liquid can mix and then unmix upon shaking and standing. But if the gas dissolves on shaking, it will not come out of solution on standing. In the flask, moreover, the change in color indicates the formation of a new chemical species —the blue material. This is formed when the gas and liquid come together. According to the chemical axiom cited above, then, the blue product will not automatically disappear to regenerate the starting materials without some change in conditions, or without reaction with some further substance. Chemical reactions are, in general, reversible, but not in the sense of first proceeding to a large extent in one direction—like forming the blue substance—and then, without a change in conditions, proceeding back to the original reactants.)

If the gas is not first entering the solution and then leaving it, but is only entering the solution, we must conclude that it is used up in the solution. If the gas is used up, the pressure of the gas above the solution should be decreasing. This is readily checked by wetting the inside of the stopper by shaking, then gently easing the stopper out of the mouth of the flask. Air will be seen to bubble into the flask through the liquid seal around the stopper. The gas pressure inside the flask has decreased, indicating that the gas is used up in the reactions.

All further experiments would confirm that one of the substances in air is required for the reaction and is consumed during the reaction. Thus the bluing reaction is indeed represented by the expression:

$$\text{gas (i.e., something in air)} + \text{liquid} \rightarrow \text{blue}$$

And we have established that the debluing reaction is not simply the reverse of this process. Thus there must be something else, let's call it X, reacting with the blue material to produce colorless products. A possible expression would be:

$$\text{blue} + X \rightarrow \text{colorless}$$

Observation and Interpretation of Rates of Reactions

Although we have not commented upon them, you may have noticed certain other features of the reaction. For example, the blue color does not appear instantly upon shaking. Several seconds elapse as it forms. The length of time the solution remains blue depends on the extent of the shaking, and appears, in fact, to be directly proportional to the shaking time. Table 2.1 shows some student data on this reaction. If two shakes produce 25 seconds of blue, four shakes will produce the color about twice as long, six shakes about three times as long, etc.

Table 2.1   SOME RESULTS ON THE RATE
OF THE DEBLUING REACTION

Number of shakes	2	3	4	5	6
Length of "blue" (sec ±2)	25	32	45	60	72
Seconds of blue/shake	13	11	11	12	12

Remarkably, however, the *intensity* of the blue color does not depend on the length of shaking. Even one shake will develop the full blue color. Further shaking does not deepen the color, but only extends the time the system remains blue. (The observations are graphed in Figure 2.2.)

These observations which are a function of time are typical of those used in studying the rates of chemical reactions. And a study of the rate of a chemical reaction is a powerful method of determining the mechanism, that is, the series of steps by which the reactants change in forming the final products.

Remember that bluing occurs only when the gas and liquid come into contact. For two atoms, or two molecules, to react (make or break chemical bonds), the atoms or molecules must collide. Any factor which affects the number or type of molecular collisions is apt to affect the rate of the reaction. Furthermore, since the mechanism of the reaction must indicate which molecules collide, and in what sequence the collisions occur to produce the final products, the rate of the reaction should be intimately related to the mechanism.

So far we have shown that the first step in the reaction mechanism in the flask is the dissolution of some gas in the liquid. This occurs upon shaking. But the color does not change instantly. This we can attribute to the necessity of a collision between molecules of the dissolved gas and molecules of some substance in the liquid that will react with the gas to produce the blue color. That this reaction is not instantaneous (of course, no reaction can be truly *instantaneous,* since the occurrence of collisions

FIGURE *2.2   The blue color increases rapidly soon after shaking, then becomes constant for some time. The length of time the intensity of the blue remains constant depends on the amount of shaking. The maximum intensity of the blue is independent of the amount of shaking. Finally the liquid becomes colorless again (see Table 2.1).*

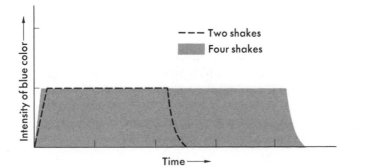

requires time) means that time is required to produce a sufficient number of collisions to give a noticeable concentration of the blue substance.

We might represent the first two steps in our proposed mechanism as

$$\text{gas (in air)} \rightarrow \text{gas (dissolved in liquid)} \tag{2.1}$$

$$\text{gas (dissolved in liquid)} + \text{liquid} \rightarrow \text{blue} \tag{2.2}$$

One might think that shaking longer would introduce more gas into the liquid through reaction 2.1. This should lead to more collisions and produce more of the blue substance through reaction 2.2. But the intensity of the blue color—which is a measure of the concentration of the blue substance—is not affected by the amount of shaking, even though more gas dissolves. (See Figure 2.2.)

Notice, however, in equation 2.2 that two substances are required to produce the blue color—both the dissolved gas and something from the liquid. Perhaps the amount of blue is determined, not by the amount of dissolved gas, but by the amount of material present in the liquid with which the dissolved gas can react. Let's represent these two substances by G for the dissolved gas, and Y for the substance it reacts with in the liquid, to give the blue material B. Reaction 2.2 above then can be written

$$G + Y \rightarrow B \tag{2.3}$$

We interpret the maximum obtainable level of blue color as an indication that Y is a limiting reagent. Regardless of the amount of G in the system, one cannot form more B at any one time than can be produced by the Y originally present. Since shaking surely does not introduce very much G into the system (the pressure of gas falls only slightly) the concentration of Y in the solution must be quite small.

We still have not accounted for the fact that more vigorous shaking lengthens the time the *constant* blue color remains.

Some Suggestions as to the Reaction

It seems reasonable that the effect of increased shaking is to increase similarly the amount of gas which dissolves. Since the gas is eventually consumed it seems reasonable that the presence of more gas should require more time for its consumption. But we have assumed in equation 2.3 that one step in this process is reaction with Y, and have also interpreted our experimental observations as indicating that there is less Y than G

present. How does the rest of the dissolved gas react in such a fashion that the concentration of the blue material is kept constant throughout the reaction. One possibility is

Bluing reaction: $$G + Y \xrightarrow{\text{fast}} B \qquad (2.4)$$

Debluing reaction: $$B + X \xrightarrow{\text{slow}} Y + \text{colorless products} \qquad (2.5)$$

We already know that while reaction 2.4 is not instantaneous, it is far more rapid than reaction 2.5. Remember that the bluing reaction takes far less time than the debluing reaction. Thus, if reaction 2.5 regenerates Y rather slowly, the regenerated Y will react quickly with any dissolved gas, G, to form B, and thus maintain the blue color at a constant level as long as G is present in the solution. Eventually, in the absence of shaking, the concentration of G will fall to the point where it is insufficient to convert further Y into B and the solution will turn colorless until further shaking introduces additional G.

The over-all rate of the debluing reaction is determined by the rate of the slow step, 2.5, since 2.4 cannot continue until 2.5 regenerates Y.

Most mechanisms have one step, such as 2.5, which is considerably slower than any of the others. It is, then, this slow step which determines the over-all rate of reaction.

The situation is analogous to that in an office. An executive can read letters and dictate answers far more rapidly than a secretary can type the required responses. Hiring more executives gets no more work done. Hiring more secretaries does. Hence in large offices the secretaries outnumber the executives in sufficient numbers that correspondence moves smoothly and does not pile up at some "rate-determining step." In a research lab, on the other hand, a single researcher cannot supply enough data to keep a secretary busy recording it. Thus, the researchers outnumber the secretaries if everyone is to operate at maximum ability. In any sequential operation, the over-all rate will be determined by the rate of the slowest step. The system will then necessarily readjust so that the concentrations of the reactants in this slowest step tend to increase. Up to a point this increases the likelihood of reaction occurring by increasing the frequency of collisions. (The secretary is faced more often with a letter to type. But a given secretary can type only so many letters per day, regardless of how many are put on her desk. If this number is exceeded, work piles up. Her speed alone then limits the work that gets done, regardless of any increase in the "concentration" of letters to be answered.) In general, the over-all rate is determined by the concentrations of one or more of the reactants in the rate-determining step.

The proposed mechanism, I, for the reaction in the flask is, then:

$$\text{gas} \xrightarrow{\text{fast}} G \tag{2.6}$$

$$G + Y \xrightarrow{\text{fast}} B \tag{2.7}$$

$$B + X \xrightarrow{\text{slow}} Y + \text{colorless products} \tag{2.8}$$

Net reaction: $\qquad$ $\text{gas} + X \xrightarrow{\text{slow}} \text{colorless products}$ $\qquad$ (2.9)

Remember: G = dissolved gas; Y = a colorless reactant originally in the solution; B = blue material formed; X = a second colorless reactant in the original solution.

If our analysis is correct it should be possible to increase the rate of the net reaction in the flask by increasing the concentration of X, since X is involved in the slow step. In fact, doubling the concentration of X should double its rate of collision with B. This should double the rate of the slow reaction 2.8, and thus double the over-all rate. In chemical terms, X proves to be glucose and it is indeed true that doubling the concentration of glucose doubles the over-all rate of reaction. Similarly, doubling the concentration of B in reaction 2.8 should double the rate of this slowest step and, thus, double the over-all rate of reaction. But B is an intermediate in the reaction mechanism. How can we double its concentration? One way is to remember that the concentration of B (causing the blue color) was determined by the limiting concentration of Y. If we double the initial concentration of Y and shake to give plenty of G, the concentration of B should double. Experiment shows that this is true. The intensity of the blue color and the rate of the net reaction both double when the initial concentration of Y (which turns out to be methylene blue) is doubled. In the presence of excess G, essentially all the Y is rapidly converted to B and the actual concentration of B equals the initial concentration of Y.

On the other hand, since Y is a limiting reagent, increasing the concentration of G has no effect on the over-all rate of reaction. Increasing the concentration of G increases the concentration neither of B nor X, the rate-determining ingredients. Thus, the concentration of G has no effect on the rate of the net reaction. Doubling the concentration of G merely means that twice as much time will be required for the over-all reaction, since twice as many molecules of G must be removed at an unchanged rate.

A Check on the Proposed Mechanism

Our proposed mechanism (I) now accounts for all of our experimental observations. It also shows the role of each ingredient present in the flask, with the exception of the sodium hydroxide. Using chemical terms, the water supplies a fluid medium for the reaction so that molecules of the colorless form of methylene blue (Y) can collide with molecules of dissolved gas (oxygen from the air). The resulting blue intermediate (B) then is assumed to collide with glucose (X) to give colorless products and regenerate the colorless form of the methylene blue (Y). Study of the effects of changing the concentrations of any of these three reactants is consistent with the proposed mechanism. Why then is sodium hydroxide present?

Suppose we experiment with changing the concentration of the sodium hydroxide. Surprisingly, doubling the concentration of the hydroxide ion doubles the rate of the reaction. (As might be expected, the sodium ion turns out to be inert in the reaction.) Yet, experiment also shows that the concentration of hydroxide ion is unchanged during the reaction. A possible interpretation of this fact is consistent with the fact that glucose, heretofore called X, can act as a weak acid, forming a low concentration of glucose anions in basic solutions. This reaction comes quickly to equilibrium and is rapid and readily reversible. We may write the equation

$$X + OH^- \rightleftharpoons X^- + H_2O$$

If we change symbolism slightly, the conservation of atoms becomes more apparent. We shall write glucose as GlOH, rather than X. Then the equation becomes

$$GlOH + OH^- \overset{a}{\underset{b}{\rightleftharpoons}} GlO^- + H_2O \qquad (2.10)$$

When a chemical system comes to a rapidly reversible equilibrium (in which both the forward (a) and reverse (b) reactions are proceeding at equally rapid rates determined by the concentrations of the reactants) one can always write down the algebraic relation among these concentrations in terms of an equilibrium-constant expression.

Thus the rate at which GlOH and OH^- will react as in reaction 2.10a is proportional to the concentration of GlOH and to the concentration of OH^-. Changing the concentration of either GlOH or OH^- would change by a similar amount the likelihood of their colliding. Thus

$$\text{rate}_a = k_a \, (\text{GlOH}) \, (\text{OH}^-) \tag{2.10a}$$

Here k_a is a constant (the proportionality constant) and the quantities in parentheses represent the concentrations of GlOH and of OH^- in the solution.

Similarly, the rate of reaction 2.10b may be represented by the equation

$$\text{rate}_b = k_b \, (\text{GlO}^-) \, (\text{H}_2\text{O}) \tag{2.10b}$$

where k_b is the proportionality constant for reaction 2.10b and the quantities in parentheses represent the concentrations of GlO^- and H_2O respectively.

But at equilibrium the two rates must be equal (since no further net change occurs). Thus

$$\text{rate}_a = \text{rate}_b \tag{2.10c}$$

and

$$k_a \, (\text{GlOH}) \, (\text{OH}^-) = k_b \, (\text{GlO}^-) \, (\text{H}_2\text{O}) \tag{2.10d}$$

Rearrangement gives

$$\frac{(\text{GlO}^-) \, (\text{H}_2\text{O})}{(\text{GlOH}) \, (\text{OH}^-)} = \frac{k_a}{k_b} = K' \tag{2.10e}$$

where K' is a new constant (equal to k_a/k_b). Since the concentration of water is very large (about 55 moles/liter) it may be treated as a constant which does not change during the reaction. We then get the algebraic relationship

$$\frac{(\text{GlO}^-)}{(\text{GlOH}) \, (\text{OH}^-)} = \frac{K'}{(\text{H}_2\text{O})} = K \tag{2.11}$$

K is called the *equilibrium constant* for reaction 2.10. Remember, the expressions in parentheses represent the concentrations of the respective substances, measured in moles per liter of solution, and the K is a numerical constant at any given temperature. The value of K is independent of the concentrations. We find experimentally that this algebraic relationship among the concentrations is maintained.

Now suppose it is not actually the glucose molecules but is, rather, the glucoside ions that react in the slow step, 2.8, of the mechanism. The equation for reaction 2.8 then becomes

$$B + GlO^- \rightarrow Y + \text{colorless products} \qquad (2.12)$$

and the rate becomes proportional to the concentration of glucoside ions. From equation 2.11 we see that the concentration of glucoside ions is given by

$$(GlO^-) = K \, (GlOH) \, (OH^-) \qquad (2.13)$$

Since glucose is a weak acid, only a small fraction will be in the form of the glucoside ion. The concentration of the glucoside ion will then be proportional to the concentration of glucose and to the concentration of hydroxide ion. Doubling the concentration of hydroxide will double the concentration of glucoside ions and thus double the rate of reaction 2.12 consistent with the experimental results. Since hydroxide ions are not consumed they must be one of the colorless products.

Another Proposed Mechanism

We now presume the total mechanism to be

oxygen gas $\rightarrow$ oxygen dissolved in water

oxygen dissolved in water + colorless methylene blue $\rightarrow$ blue methylene blue

glucose + hydroxide ion $\rightleftharpoons$ glucoside ion + water

glucoside ion + blue methylene blue $\rightarrow$ colorless methylene blue + hydroxide ion + colorless products

Net: oxygen gas + glucose $\rightarrow$ colorless products

or, in schematic chemical symbols (the detailed formulas are not important here), our proposed mechanism II is

$$O_{2(g)} \xrightarrow{\text{fast}} O_{2(aq)} \qquad (2.14)$$

$$O_{2(aq)} + \underset{\text{colorless}}{MeBl} \xrightarrow{\text{fast}} \underset{\text{blue}}{MeBl} \text{ (all aqueous)} \qquad (2.15)$$

$$GlOH + OH^- \overset{fast}{\rightleftharpoons} GlO^- + H_2O \text{ (all aqueous)} \qquad (2.16)$$

$$GlO^- + MeBl \overset{slow}{\longrightarrow} MeBl + OH^- + \text{colorless products} \qquad (2.17)$$
$$\underset{\text{blue}}{} \quad \underset{\text{colorless}}{} \qquad \text{(all aqueous)}$$

Net: $\qquad O_{2(g)} + GlOH_{(aq)} \overset{slow}{\longrightarrow} \text{colorless products}_{(aq)} \qquad (2.18)$

We have found experimentally that the actual rate of reaction is given by the expression

$$\text{rate of reaction} = k \ (MeBl)(GlOH)(OH^-) \qquad (2.19)$$

This states that the rate of the net reaction is equal to k, a constant at any given temperature independent of concentration, times the concentrations of methylene blue, glucose, and hydroxide ion, respectively. Changing one or more of these concentrations changes the rate of reaction accordingly.

The experimental rate equation, 2.19, is completely consistent with the suggested mechanism and the recorded experimental facts. (Here, as in many mechanisms, there are actually some complications we have not discussed. But it is still true that, within the observed experimental data, mechanism II accounts for the observations. As a matter of general fact one can never be completely sure of the validity of any suggested mechanism. There may be another undiscovered possibility that would fit the facts as well. Since mechanisms must be inferred from experimental data, such as data on rates, the most one can expect is that the mechanism be consistent with all the observable data and thus have a high probability of being correct. On the other hand it is true that many mechanisms can be eliminated from consideration and shown to be impossible since they do not fit the experimental data.)

In the system we have studied, changes in the concentration of one of the net reactants, glucose, affect the rate of reaction while changes in the concentration of the other reactant in the net equation, oxygen, have no effect on the rate. This indicates that glucose, or some substance whose concentration is determined by it, is involved in the rate-determining mechanistic step but that oxygen is not.

Catalysts

Changes in the concentration of two other substances, methylene blue and hydroxide ion, also affect the rate, despite the fact these two substances are not consumed in the net reaction. This would indicate that these substances, or some substances whose concentrations are determined by them, are involved in the slow, rate-determining step, but that these two substances are then regenerated in other steps of the reaction. Substances whose presence affects the rate of reaction, but whose concentration is not affected by the net reaction are called catalysts. The reaction we have studied is one of only a few reactions in which one can visually observe the role of the catalyst. In this instance (as in general) the catalyst forms an intermediate (the blue substance), which then reacts in the slow step of the reaction regenerating the catalyst.

The Effect of Temperature on Rate

One further variable can be easily investigated in this system—the effect of changing the temperature. By having several flasks at different temperatures but otherwise identical, we may easily show that the rate increases markedly when the temperature increases. See Table 2.2 for some student data.

Table 2.2   TIME THE FLASK REMAINED BLUE
WHEN CONCENTRATIONS, INCLUDING AMOUNT OF ADDED OXYGEN,
WERE HELD CONSTANT AND TEMPERATURE WAS VARIED

Temperature °K (± 0.5°)	Length of "Blue" Sec (± 3 Sec)
283	630
288	305
292	152
298	60.6
306	17.3
316	7.5

One is tempted to believe that the increase in rate is caused by the increase in molecular velocities at the higher temperatures. Such an increase in molecular velocities will increase the number of molecular collisions per second and so increase the rate. It is easy to show, however, that the increase in rate is far greater than can be accounted for by an increased number of collisions. (Table 2.2 shows that a 10 degree rise in temperature increases the rate of this reaction about fourfold in the experimental range studied.) We shall discuss this effect of temperature in the next chapter, but you might try to suggest a reasonable explanation of the effect before reading the chapter.

Summary

We have discovered experimentally that molecular collisions are required if chemical reactions are to occur. The number of collisions per second and hence the rate of any reaction is proportional to the concentrations of the reacting molecules. The rate is also affected by a change in temperature. Changing certain concentrations affects the rate of reaction and provides evidence concerning the slowest step in the mechanism. From these rate data and other observations it is often possible to propose a series of rather simple chemical reactions which occur in sequence and account for the over-all net reaction. Most commonly these mechanistic steps involve collisions between two molecules and relatively simple changes in the colliding molecules. The over-all complex reaction is thus accomplished by a series of much simpler sequential steps.

Questions

1. When we first light the wick of a previously used candle, a large flame usually forms. This flame quickly diminishes in size and then flares up again to a full candle flame. Check this observation experimentally. If it does not check consider why. How do you account for the observations in terms of the mechanism of burning?

2. When we insert a slotted, flat piece of aluminum foil around the base of the wick of a burning candle, the flame often diminishes slowly in size, then flares up, then diminishes slowly only to flare up again. The aluminum foil shows no apparent change. This fluctuating behavior can continue for 10 to 15 minutes or more. How do you account for these observations in terms of the mechanism of burning?

3. Outline a possible mechanism and a probable rate-determining step for each of the following changes:
   a. Burning of a piece of wood
   b. Conversion of a cloud into rain
   c. Curing a disease

4. Evaluate the following proposed mechanism for the "blue bottle" reactions. That is, which experimental data, if any, does it fit, and which, if any, does it not fit.

   $$\text{gas} \rightarrow G \qquad \text{(a)}$$
   $$G + Y \rightarrow B \qquad \text{(b)}$$
   $$B + X \rightarrow Y \qquad \text{(c)}$$

5. The rate of the following reaction in dilute aqueous solution:

$$(C_6H_{11}O_5)_2O + H_2O \rightarrow 2\, C_6H_{11}O_5OH$$

is given by the equation:

rate of disappearance of $(C_6H_{11}O_5)_2O = k\,[(C_6H_{11}O_5)_2O]\,[H^+]$

Suggest a possible mechanism for this reaction, indicating the relative rates of each step.

6. Is either of the following a reasonable mechanism for the reaction discussed in problem 5 above?

Mechanism A: $\overset{\text{fast}}{H^+ + H_2O \rightleftharpoons H_3O^+}$

$$\overset{\text{slow}}{(C_6H_{11}O_5)_2O + H_2O \rightarrow 2\, C_6H_{11}O_5OH}$$

Mechanism B: $\overset{\text{fast}}{H^+ + H_2O \rightleftharpoons H_3O^+}$

$$\overset{\text{slow}}{H_3O^+ + (C_6H_{11}O_5)_2O \rightarrow C_6H_{11}O_5OH + C_6H_{11}O_5OH_2^+}$$

$$\overset{\text{fast}}{H_2O + C_6H_{11}O_5OH_2^+ \rightarrow C_6H_{11}O_5OH + H_3O^+}$$

7. Which of the following is the "best guess" for the time of debluing at a temperature of $295°K$ under the conditions used in obtaining the data in Table 2.2: 90, 105, or 120 seconds?

3

Molecular Collisions

As we have seen from the experimental evidence in the preceding chapter, molecular collisions must always precede chemical reaction. Yet the rate of molecular collisions in solids, liquids, and gases at ordinary pressures is so great that all reactions would be very rapid were it only necessary for collisions to occur. No reaction can proceed more rapidly than molecular collisions allow, but many reactions proceed much more slowly. Apparently not every molecular collision leads to reaction.

We can study simple molecular collisions more readily in gases than in liquids or solids. At ordinary laboratory conditions, less than 1 per cent of the volume of a gas is "occupied" by the gas molecules. The greater part of the volume is free space. Under these conditions it proves very unlikely that three molecules will ever collide simultaneously. Each molecule hits other molecules about 10^9 (1 billion) times per sec in bimolecular collisions, but a molecule undergoes a trimolecular collision only perhaps 10^5 times per sec, and collisions between larger numbers of molecules occur correspondingly less often. Thus reactions which proceed in the gaseous state must, for the most part, proceed by bimolecular mechanistic steps. The number of such collisions, as we have already found experimentally, increases with the concentrations of the molecules. Now we shall look at further details of these collisions.

Average Molecular Velocities

If we place aqueous solutions of hydrogen chloride and ammonia (giving equal concentrations of ammonia and hydrogen chloride gas) at opposite ends of a closed glass tube one meter long, we observe, after about 30 minutes, that a ring of solid ammonium chloride forms within the tube. (See Figure 3.1.) Since the concentrations of the two gases were the same, this must mean that the ammonia molecules travel faster than the hydrogen chloride ones. Careful measurement shows that the ammonia covers about 1.4 times the distance the hydrogen chloride does in the same time. Thus ammonia molecules must, on the average, be moving about 1.4 times as fast.

A similar result is obtained with the apparatus illustrated in Figure 3.2. The hydrogen escapes most rapidly, the helium next, the oxygen next, the

FIGURE *3.1   When two tufts of cotton are wet with concentrated aqueous ammonia and hydrogen chloride, respectively, and then placed at opposite ends of a closed tube, a ring of solid ammonium chloride dust eventually forms where the ammonia molecules meet the hydrogen chloride molecules on the hydrogen chloride side of the middle of the tube. Ammonia molecules, on the average, move 1.4 times as far as the hydrogen chloride molecules. Hence, on the average, the ammonia molecules must have a velocity 1.4 times greater than that of the hydrogen chloride molecules.*

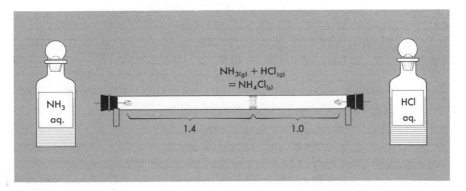

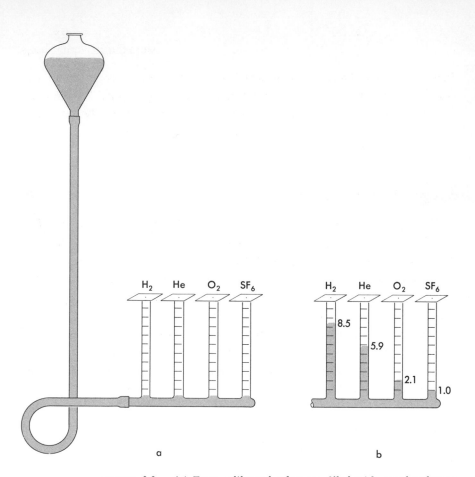

FIGURE 3.2 (a) Four calibrated tubes are filled with equal volumes of gaseous hydrogen, helium, oxygen, and sulfur hexafluoride, respectively. Pressure is maintained by a column of mercury. Each tube is topped by a thin foil containing identical small pin holes through which gaseous molecules can effuse. Any gaseous molecules striking a pin hole will escape from the tube. At constant pressure and temperature the number of molecules striking each pin hole per second will be determined by the molecular velocities. Thus, the volume of gas which escapes in each tube will be proportional to the molecular velocity of that gas. (b) During effusion the liquid levels rise and we see that the ratio of volumes of escaped gas (and, hence, the ratio of the molecular velocities) is 8.5/5.9/2.1/1.0 for H_2, He, O_2, and SF_6, respectively.

sulfur hexafluoride least rapidly. The ratios of their rates of escape, hence the ratios of their average molecular velocities, are $H_2/He/O_2/SF_6 =$ 8.5/5.9/2.1/1.0. The only molecular property which correlates well with these ratios is molecular weight. For each set of gases, squaring the relative molecular velocities and multiplying by the corresponding molecular weights gives a constant value as shown in Table 3.1.

Table 3.1 RELATIONSHIP BETWEEN MOLECULAR WEIGHT
AND RELATIVE MOLECULAR VELOCITY

	HCl	NH_3	SF_6	O_2	He	H_2
Molar weight (M)	36.5	17.0	146	32.0	4.0	20
Relative velocity (v)	1.00	1.45	1.0	2.1	5.9	8.5
Relative velocity squared (v^2)	1.00	2.10	1.0	4.4	35	72
Mv^2 (constant value)	36.5	35.8	146	141	140	146

This relationship, $Mv^2 =$ constant, holds in fact for all gases at any given temperature. When either of these experiments is run at other temperatures, the same relative velocities are obtained, but the absolute velocity of each gas increases with temperature. If we express the molecular weight in grams per mole, the average velocity in centimeters per second, and the temperature in degrees Kelvin, the following equation is found to apply to all gases. (Data for H_2 at 27°C are used to evaluate the constant. Note that the constant, 2.7×10^8, has the dimensions of g $\times$ cm^2/mole $\times$ °K $\times$ sec^2, or ergs/mole $\times$ °K.)

$$\frac{Mv^2}{T} = \text{constant} = \frac{2.0 \text{ (g/mole)} \times (2.0 \times 10^5)^2 \text{ (cm/sec)}^2}{300 \text{ (°K)}}$$

$$\frac{Mv^2}{T} = 2.7 \times 10^8 \frac{\text{g cm}^2}{\text{mole sec}^2 \text{ °K}} \tag{3.1}$$

Average molecular velocities depend on the absolute temperature and the molecular weight. Thus we expect gases with low molecular weights to have higher velocities, to make more collisions per second, and, possibly, to react at higher rates because of this larger number of molecular collisions. This is partly offset by the generally larger size of heavier molecules.

We also expect an increase in temperature to increase the number of molecular collisions and also to increase the rates of chemical reactions. Doubling the absolute temperature of a gas (e.g., changing the temperature from 27°C to 327°C) should increase the average molecular velocity by the square root of 2, or 1.4 times. One might expect the reaction velocity to be 1.4 times greater at the higher temperature. Actually the reaction rate is usually thousands of times greater at the higher temperature, a fact not anticipated by our knowledge of average molecular velocities.

MOLECULAR COLLISIONS

This very large effect of temperature on rate observed in most experiments is consistent with the similar result discovered in our methylene blue system where a small rise in temperature had a marked effect on the reaction rate. (See Table 2.2.)

Effect of Temperature on Rate Constant, k

The rate of any chemical reaction is found to obey an equation of the general type

$$\text{rate} = k \times \text{(some function of the concentrations of the reactants)} \quad (3.2)$$

In the methylene blue case, the corresponding rate equation was

$$\text{rate} = k \text{ (glucose) (methylene blue) (hydroxide ion)} \quad (3.3)$$

In each such equation, k is a constant at any one temperature, but varies with the temperature. Table 3.2 indicates how the k's for several reactions change with the temperature. Note the rapid variation in k as the

Table 3.2 VARIATION OF RATE CONSTANTS WITH KELVIN TEMPERATURE

Reaction

$H_2 + I_2 \rightarrow 2 HI$	T	556	575	629	666	700	781
	k	4.45×10^{-5}	1.37×10^{-4}	2.52×10^{-3}	1.41×10^{-2}	6.43×10^{-2}	1.34
$2 HI \rightarrow H_2 + I_2$	T	556	575	629	666	700	781
	k	7.04×10^{-7}	2.44×10^{-6}	6.04×10^{-5}	4.38×10^{-4}	2.32×10^{-3}	7.90×10^{-2}
$Br + H_2 \rightarrow HBr + H$	T	498.9	524.6	549.0	550.7	574.5	612.1
	k	1.16×10^3	3.11×10^3	5.62×10^3	6.61×10^3	1.47×10^4	3.01×10^4
$N_2O_5 \rightarrow N_2O_4 + \frac{1}{2} O_2$	T	273	293	308	318	328	338
	k	7.87×10^{-7}	1.76×10^{-5}	1.35×10^{-4}	4.98×10^{-4}	1.50×10^{-3}	4.87×10^{-3}
$Br_2 + 2 NO \rightarrow 2 NOBr$	T	265.2	273.7	288.0			
	k	2.12×10^3	2.35×10^3	2.68×10^3			

temperature is changed. By plotting various functions of k against various functions of T one can discover empirically, as in Figure 3.3, that plots of log k versus $1/T$ give straight lines over large ranges in T. The equation of these empirically discovered straight lines is always of the form

$$\log k = \frac{A}{T} + B \quad (3.4)$$

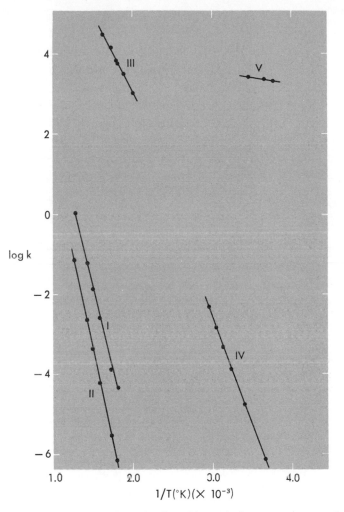

FIGURE 3.3 *When the logarithm of the rate constant is plotted against the reciprocal of the Kelvin temperature, a straight line is obtained. The equation of this empirically obtained straight line is* $\log k = \dfrac{A}{T} + B$ *where A is the slope of the line and B is another constant.*

I.	$H_2 + I_2 \rightarrow 2\,HI$
II.	$2\,HI \rightarrow H_2 + I_2$
III.	$Br + H_2 \rightarrow HBr + H$
IV.	$N_2O_5 \rightarrow N_2O_4 + \frac{1}{2}\,O_2$
V.	$Br_2 + 2\,NO \rightarrow 2\,NOBr$

where A is a constant equal to the slope of the log k versus $1/T$ plot, and B is another constant.

Now we must remember that molecules not only hit more often if they are traveling faster, but they also hit harder. Since chemical reactions involve the making and breaking of chemical bonds which are due to the attractive forces between the atoms, it seems reasonable that the force a molecule experiences during a collision would affect the likelihood of reaction. We shall see that our empirically discovered plots are consistent with this idea, but first we must examine more closely the question of actual molecular velocities, not just average molecular velocities.

Actual Molecular Velocities

Studying the bulk properties of a substance—such as molecular weight by gas-density methods, or molecular velocities by effusion rates of large quantities of gases—must perforce give average values for these quantities. For example, the discovery of isotopes of most of the elements had to wait until methods were available for detecting events produced by single atoms and molecules. Similarly, the measurement of individual molecular velocities came later than the measurement of average molecular velocities. Actually, in this case Maxwell and Boltzmann independently predicted that the velocities in any gas should vary considerably from the average, and before any experimental work was performed they calculated the distribution to be expected in molecular velocities. (See Figure 3.4.)

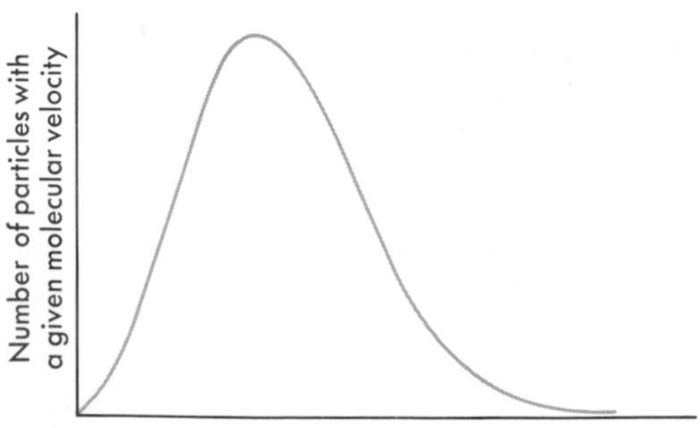

Their general argument was that even if at one instant the actual molecular velocities in a collection of gaseous molecules were identical, a short time later a large spread of velocities would be found. This follows from the fact that the molecular collisions are random and will involve the transfer of various amounts of energy depending on the angle of collision. Consideration of all possible collisions among particles allows one to derive the theoretical curves of Maxwell and Boltzmann.

The results of subsequent experiments fully agreed with the theory

FIGURE *3.4   The Maxwell and Boltzmann prediction of the number of molecules having particular molecular velocities. Notice that very few molecules have low velocities, that a range of velocities represented by the peak of the curve accounts for most of the molecules, but that a large number of molecules have velocities higher than this, and that an appreciable number of molecules have very high velocities compared to the average.*

Number of particles with a given molecular velocity

Molecular velocity

and led to its rapid acceptance. Figure 3.5 shows an experimental arrangement for obtaining data on the actual molecular velocities. Data obtained from such experiments fit the theoretical curves within the limit of experimental errors.

Only a small fraction of the molecules actually have the average molecular velocity. Most of the molecules have velocities either less than or more than the average velocity. A few molecules are almost stationary at any instant and others are moving at velocities twice as great as the average or even faster. These rapidly moving molecules, of course, have high individual kinetic energies (kinetic energy $= \frac{1}{2} mv^2$) associated with their motions and make very forceful collisions with other molecules. These collisions are far more apt to lead to reaction than collisions between molecules having the average velocities.

One of the quantitative predictions of the Maxwell-Boltzmann theory was that for any large number of molecules, N_o, the number, N, of molecules having kinetic energy greater than any particular value of $E = \frac{1}{2} mv^2$ (where m is the molar weight and v is the molecular velocity) is proportional to $e^{-\frac{1}{2} mv^2/RT}$. (e is the natural base of logarithms, and R is a constant.) Thus

$$N/N_o = De^{-\frac{1}{2} mv^2/RT} \tag{3.5}$$

where D is a constant. As T increases, the fraction of molecules having high energies can increase very rapidly, as shown in the exponential expression, and in Figure 3.6.

Molecular Velocities and Reaction Rates

You will remember the empirical discovery mentioned on page 28 that the relationship between the reaction rate constant, k, and the absolute temperature, T, is given by equation 3.4

$$\log k = \frac{A}{T} + B \tag{3.4}$$

where A and B are constants independent of the temperature or concentrations. Equation 3.4 can be written in the equivalent form

$$k = Fe^{-E/RT} \tag{3.6}$$

where F, E, and R are constants independent of the temperature or concentrations. Comparing equations 3.5 and 3.6 shows that each contains

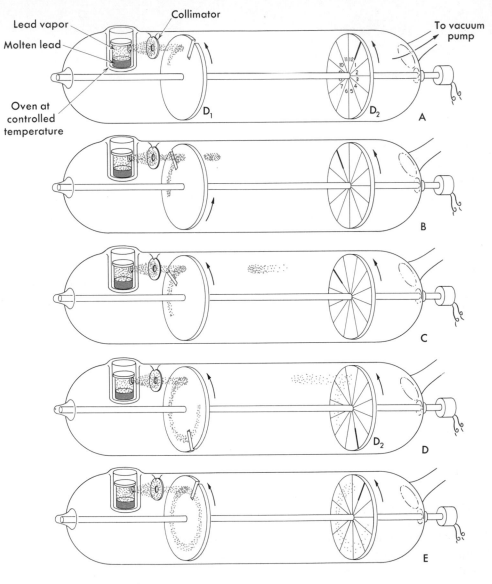

Lead vapor

Molten lead

Collimator

To vacuum pump

Oven at controlled temperature

D_1

D_2

A

B

C

D_2

D

E

a

FIGURE 3.5   (a) An oven and revolving disc assembly for determining the molecular velocity distribution in a condensable gas; (b) on facing page, the receiver disc after many revolutions; (c) on facing page, plot of weight of lead deposited in each sector of the disc after many revolutions. The solid line is the curve theoretically predicted by Maxwell and Boltzmann. Notice the excellent agreement between experiment and theory.

an exponential term involving the reciprocal of the absolute temperature. Perhaps this is more than a coincidence.

We have already alluded to the idea that the likelihood of reaction upon the collision of two molecules must certainly be affected by the force of the collision. Forceful collisions are much more apt to lead to the breaking and making of chemical bonds than are less forceful collisions. In fact, it seems intuitively acceptable to believe that some minimum force would be required for reaction to occur. After all, a certain minimum force is necessary to break a piece of wood apart, or to drive a nail. The same might hold in chemical reactions.

If a certain minimum force of collision is necessary, molecules with less than sufficient energy to exert this force will not react, whereas molecules with a higher energy than this minimum can react. But equation 3.5 gives the fraction of molecules with kinetic energy greater than any

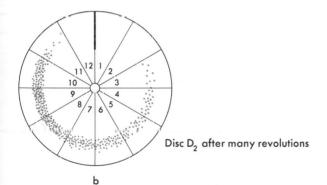

Disc D$_2$ after many revolutions

b

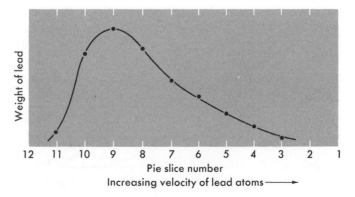

Weight of lead

12   11   10   9   8   7   6   5   4   3   2   1

Pie slice number

Increasing velocity of lead atoms ⟶

c

selected amount, $\frac{1}{2} mv^2$. And equation 3.6 gives the relation between the rate of reaction and the absolute temperature. Continuing our assumption that there is indeed a minimum amount of energy required before a molecule can react upon collision we may define this quantity of energy necessary to activate the molecule to the point where it can react as the *activation energy*, $\triangle E^{\ddagger}$. (This quantity can be read as "delta E double-dagger.") If the activation energy is all kinetic energy, we have

$$\triangle E^{\ddagger} = (\tfrac{1}{2} mv^2)^{\ddagger} \tag{3.7}$$

where the quantity $(\tfrac{1}{2} mv^2)^{\ddagger}$ represents the minimum kinetic energy required for the molecule to react.

According to equation 3.5 the fraction, N/N_o, of all the molecules which will have this activation energy, or more energy, is given by:

$$N/N_o = De^{-(\tfrac{1}{2} mv^2)^{\ddagger}/RT} \tag{3.8}$$

By using equation 3.7, equation 3.8 is converted to equation 3.9.

$$N/N_o = De^{-\triangle E^{\ddagger}/RT} \tag{3.9}$$

FIGURE 3.6 *Distribution of molecular kinetic energies at three different temperatures, T_3 greater than T_2, T_2 greater than T_1. Notice that at the higher temperatures there are not only fewer molecules with low energies, but there are many more with high energies. The number with energies greater than some selected high energy, such as E, increases rapidly as the temperature rises. Data are for oxygen gas at 100°K, 273°K, and 500°K, respectively.*

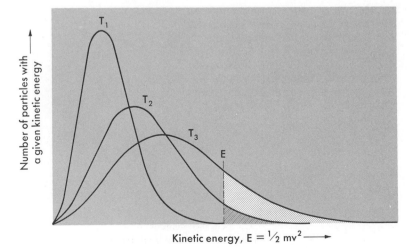

Note that the second term in equation 3.9 has exactly the same form as the second term in equation 3.6. Since this is consistent with the intuitive idea that the rate of reaction might depend on the fraction of molecules having more than the activation energy, let us substitute equation 3.9 into equation 3.6. We get

$$k = Ce^{-\Delta E^{\ddagger}/RT} \tag{3.10}$$

where k is the rate constant, $\triangle E^{\ddagger}$ is the activation energy, T is the absolute temperature, and C and R are constants independent of temperature or concentrations.

Equation 3.10 may be written in the alternative form, corresponding to equation 3.4:

$$\log k = \frac{-\triangle E^{\ddagger}}{2.303RT} + B \tag{3.11}$$

where k is the rate constant, $\triangle E^{\ddagger}$ is the activation energy for the reaction under study, T is the Kelvin temperature, and B is a constant which depends only on the reaction under study.

Comparison of equation 3.11 with Figure 3.3 shows that the slopes of the lines in the figure correspond in value to $-\triangle E^{\ddagger}/4.575$. Thus one can calculate values for $\triangle E^{\ddagger}$ by plotting values of $\log k$ versus the reciprocal of the corresponding Kelvin temperature, and measuring the slope of the resulting straight line. Some values of $\triangle E^{\ddagger}$ obtained in this way are shown in Table 3.3.

Table 3.3   SOME ACTIVATION ENERGIES

Reaction	$\triangle E^{\ddagger}$ Activation Energy in kcal
$H_2 + I_2 \rightarrow 2\,HI$	40
$2\,HI \rightarrow H_2 + I_2$	44
$CN^- + CH_3I \rightarrow CH_3CN + I^-$	20

Activation Energy and Reaction Rate

Equation 3.11 allows one to make a quantitative calculation of the activation energy if the rate constant is known as a function of the absolute temperature. But it pays to explore this relation qualitatively as well. Very fast reactions must have activation energies which are small compared to the average kinetic energies of the molecules. Under such conditions almost every molecule has sufficient energy to react and most collisions lead to reactions.

Similarly, a reaction whose rate is only slightly affected by changing the temperature must have a low activation energy. This follows from equation 3.11, which shows that the slope of the log k versus $1/T$ plot is proportional to the activation energy. If there is little change of k with T, the slope must be small and the activation energy also must be small. Many precipitation reactions have rates which are little affected by change in T, indicating small activation energies.

Reactions whose rates are greatly changed by changes in T must have high activation energies. The argument here is the same as in the preceding paragraph. The reactions involved in cooking most foods have high activation energies. Hence the great decrease in cooking time when pressure cookers are used to increase the temperature.

Experience shows that the great majority of reactions give almost linear log k versus $1/T$ plots. This greatly enhances our belief in the concept of a fixed minimum activation energy being required for each reaction. It also means, of course, that the activation energy can be calculated from values of the rate constant, k, at any two temperatures if the data are carefully taken. As with scientific data in general, so here, it is highly advisable to obtain data at more than two temperatures and so increase the certainty of the calculations.

It may have struck you in reading the paragraphs above that we have not stated that a low activation energy automatically means a fast reaction. A low activation energy merely means that there will be little effect on the rate if the temperature is changed. But is it possible that molecular collisions can occur frequently between molecules having more than enough activation energy and yet lead to no reaction? Experimentally this is not an uncommon occurrence. Many substances remain in solution (supersaturated) or in the liquid state (undercooled) for very long periods of time in spite of frequent intermolecular collisions and very low activation energies. How do we interpret this?

Molecular Collision and Molecular Geometry

In addition to energy and concentration, molecules also have size and shape. The molecular models in Figure 3.7 show this. Large molecules may have very complicated shapes. Even in small molecules the various profiles of the molecules may be quite different. Certain sides of the mole-

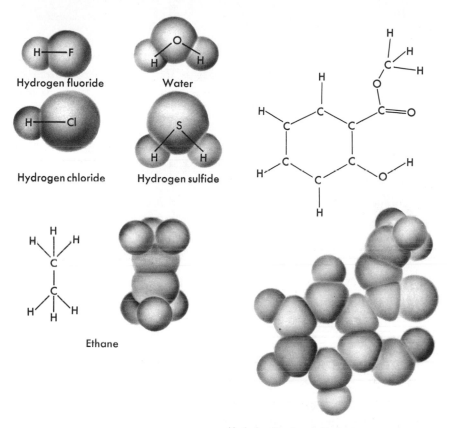

Hydrogen fluoride

Water

Hydrogen chloride

Hydrogen sulfide

Ethane

Methyl salicylate (oil of wintergreen)

FIGURE 3.7   Schematic molecular models of some well-known molecules of simple to moderate complexity. Notice that even though the different profiles may have similar geometrical features, the details of their atomic constitution, hence chemical reactivity, may be quite different.

cule may be occupied by rather unreactive atoms and other sides by highly reactive ones. Reaction can occur only when the reactive sides are involved in the collision. Collision with the unreactive side of the molecule is not nearly as apt to lead to reaction.

Of course, a highly energetic collision may break a molecule apart regardless of the orientation at the time of collision. Thus the simplest correlation between collisional energy and geometrical orientation might be to say that the activation energy varies with the geometrical orientation of the molecules at the moment of collision. Most theoretical approaches, however, treat the orientation problem merely in terms of the likelihood that a suitable orientation will occur during the collision. This likelihood is often expressed as the entropy of activation, $\triangle S^{\ddagger}$.

The entropy of activation determines the fraction of molecular collisions that have an appropriate orientation, just as the energy of activation determines the fraction of molecules that will have sufficient energy to react upon collision. Just as the likelihood of having sufficient activation energy is expressed as $e^{-\Delta E^{\ddagger}/RT}$, so the likelihood of having a suitable orientation is expressed as $e^{\Delta S^{\ddagger}/R}$. Here e is the natural base of logarithms, $\Delta S^{\ddagger}$ is the entropy of activation, and R is the same constant as in the activation energy expression.

$\Delta S^{\ddagger}$ may be expressed as

$$\Delta S^{\ddagger} = R \log \frac{(\text{number of good collisional orientations})}{(\text{total number of collisional orientations})} \qquad (3.12)$$

This ratio is often very much less than 1. Thus $\Delta S^{\ddagger}$ becomes more and more negative (i.e., the value of $\Delta S^{\ddagger}$ decreases) as the orientational requirements become more and more stringent. A less negative value of $\Delta S^{\ddagger}$ indicates that a wider variety of collisional configurations can lead to reaction.

The likelihood that a given collision will have sufficient energy for reaction is proportional to $e^{-\Delta E^{\ddagger}/RT}$. The likelihood of suitable orientation upon collision is proportional to $e^{\Delta S^{\ddagger}/R}$. The likelihood of particles simultaneously having both enough energy and a suitable orientation is proportional to the product of these two terms. Thus, the rate constant, k, is given by

$$k = Qe^{-\Delta E^{\ddagger}/RT}e^{\Delta S^{\ddagger}/R} \qquad (3.13)$$

where Q can be treated as a constant for our purposes. (Since Q relates to the number of molecular collisions per second, it must contain at least one temperature term to allow for the fact that an increase in temperature increases the number of molecular collisions per second. But this slight effect on the rate will be neglected here.)

Note that the orientation term, $\Delta S^{\ddagger}/R$, is not affected by the temperature. This is reasonable since changing the temperature has no effect on the relative orientations of the gaseous molecules.

The orientation requirements may be very stringent with complicated molecules (large negative value of $\Delta S^{\ddagger}$) and may lead to a very slow rate even though the activation energy is low and the concentrations are high enough to insure many collisions. On the other hand, substances of simple shape will normally react rapidly even at low concentrations (since they have small negative values of $\Delta S^{\ddagger}$) if their energy of activation is low. Thus, silver chloride, AgCl, precipitates as fast as silver and chloride ions (Ag^+ and Cl^- are both spherical) are mixed, but sodium acetate, $NaCH_3CO_2$, supersaturates readily since the resulting crystal, sodium acetate, has a complicated structure due to the lack of symmetry in the acetate ion, $CH_3CO_2{}^-$. (See Figure 3.8.)

Even rather simple reactions may have some hindrance to reaction due to orientation requirements. The reaction

$$H_2 + I_2 \rightarrow 2\ HI \tag{3.14}$$

is a case in point which has been very thoroughly studied.

The experimental rate equation for the reaction of gaseous hydrogen and gaseous iodine is

$$\text{rate} = k\ (H_2)\ (I_2) \tag{3.15}$$

This rate equation and all other available data are consistent with the idea that the mechanism of the reaction is a simple one. It involves a simple collision between a hydrogen molecule and an iodine molecule with the simultaneous formation of two molecules of hydrogen iodide.

In order for this simple collision to give two molecules of hydrogen iodide, however, the collision must occur with an orientation similar to that shown in Figure 3.9.

The activation energy for this reaction is high, yet the rate is even slower than expected. This is consistent with a rather apparent geometrical requirement. It has been established that a collision such as that shown in Figure 3.10 has considerably less chance of leading to reaction than that shown in Figure 3.9. End-to-end collisions, of course, would be even less likely to result in reaction.

Reactions in Condensed Phases

The arguments we have used thus far regarding activation en-

FIGURE 3.8 *Schematic molecular model of an acetate ion, $CH_3CO_2{}^-$, showing the lack of symmetry which makes it difficult to start crystallization of sodium acetate from aqueous solution. Thus, the rate of crystallization is slow compared to that of solids such as silver chloride, which contains only ions of spherical symmetry.*

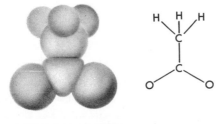

Acetate ion

ergy and entropy of activation apply strictly only to reactions in the gaseous phase since they are based on the Maxwell-Boltzmann theory of gases. However, experiments on reaction rates in liquids and solids show that the same ideas are applicable. Many reactions in condensed phases also give straight lines when log k is plotted versus $1/T$. The slope of the line can be successfully interpreted as being proportional to the activation energy. The concept of entropy of activation can also be successfully applied to these reactions in condensed phases.

FIGURE 3.9   (left) Favorable collisional orientation for reaction between an H_2 and an I_2 molecule.

FIGURE 3.10   (right) Unfavorable collisional orientation for reaction between an H_2 and an I_2 molecule. Notice that there are many more possibilities of unfavorable collisions such as this than of favorable collisions such as shown in Figure 3.9.

Somewhat less is known about the details of reactions in condensed phases compared to gases, but few new ideas seem necessary. The principal differences seem to be attributable to the restricted motions that molecules experience in condensed phases. Molecules tend to get trapped, or "caged," in certain locations, and can only with difficulty force their way out toward reactive sites. Yet the ease and reliability with which reactions proceed at a wide variety of rates in such condensed phases as living systems can also be successfully treated in terms of molecular collisions influenced by activation energy and by entropy of activation requirements.

Summary

Reactions occur, then, only when molecules (1) collide, (2) are in a suitable configuration when they collide, and (3) collide with sufficient energy to supply the activation energy. All chemical reactions must satisfy these three criteria, but the criteria do not allow one to interpret easily why certain reactions occur and others do not. The criteria do interpret rates of reactions. They indicate that reactions will proceed slowly if there are few molecular collisions occurring (low concentrations of reactants), if there is a stringent orientation requirement, or if the activation energy is very high and the temperature is low. The slow reaction between hydrogen and oxygen at room temperatures, for example, is due to a high activation energy. And the criteria allow us to understand why most reactions proceed through a series of relatively simple steps (often involving only bimolecular collisions). The over-all rate of reaction is determined by the rate of the reaction in the slowest step.

Questions

1. Consider the two gas-phase reactions

$$I_2 + H_2 \rightarrow 2\,HI$$
$$I_2 + Br_2 \rightarrow 2\,IBr$$

The entropies of activation are similar but the rates are quite different. Experimental determinations show that the activation energies are different. Allowing for this effect still leaves the H_2 reaction about nine times as fast as the Br_2 reaction at the same temperature and concentrations. Account for this nine-fold difference in rate.

2. The activation energies are similar but the rate of combustion of gaseous $CH_3CH_2CH_2CH_2CH_2CH_2CH_3$ in an automobile engine is greater than for

gaseous CH_3—$\overset{\overset{\displaystyle H}{|}}{C}$—$\overset{\overset{\displaystyle CH_3}{|}}{C}$—$CH_3$. Account for this difference.

3. Aluminum is a reactive element toward most of the nonmetallic elements. Yet when a piece of aluminum wire is dropped into pure liquid bromine, no apparent change is observed for a minute or two. This "induction period" is then followed by a very rapid, vigorous (in fact, dangerous) reaction. How do you account for this induction period?

4. When pure copper pellets are dropped into nitric acid the initial reaction is moderate. The rate increases rapidly with time, however, and can get out of hand if proper precautions are not taken. What precautions would you suggest? (Incidentally this problem of preventing increasing rates in unattended reactions is very common in chemistry and standard precautions are widely used.)

5. Use the data in Table 2.2, page 21, to calculate $\Delta E^{\ddagger}$ for the "debluing reaction."

4

The Making

and Breaking

of Chemical Bonds

Attractive forces exist between any two atoms. In this sense, any atom can form bonds to any other atom. We observe this experimentally not only in the very wide variety of chemical compounds which are known, but also in the fact that all substances condense to liquids and solids at low enough temperatures and high enough pressures. The condensation process involves the action of attractive forces between atoms and molecules. These forces must be strong enough to hold the atoms and molecules close together in spite of the random thermal jostlings due to the kinetic energies of the particles. Similarly, every substance is somewhat soluble in every other substance, indicating again that at least weak attractions must exist in all cases.

Strong and Weak Attractions

It is certainly true that not all attractive forces are equally strong. Among the strongest chemical forces which have been measured are those which hold the two atoms of nitrogen together in molecular nitrogen. We shall follow the practice of indicating the magnitude of the forces acting between particles in terms of the energy required to separate the particles completely. We call the energy required to accomplish this separation the *bond energy,* or *bond strength.* The bond strength in molecular nitrogen is 225 kcal per mole. At the other extreme is probably the attractive energy between helium atoms, approximately 0.02 kcal per mole, which is less than one ten thousandth of the nitrogen-nitrogen interaction. A continuous gradation in attractive forces is found between these extremes.

Typical values for the forces acting between certain commonly paired atoms are shown in Table 4.1. In each case the figure given measures the energy necessary to separate completely a mole of the pair of atoms.

Table 4.1   SOME INTERATOMIC BONDING ENERGIES (AT $0°K$)

Atoms	He	Hg	I	Cl	H—I	H	H—F	N
Substance	liquid helium	Hg_2	I_2	Cl_2	HI	H_2	HF	N_2
Interaction energy (kcal/mole)	0.02	1.59	35.67	57.34	71.3	103.05	134.1	224.86

Many scientists choose to divide strong and weak forces into separate categories, sometimes called chemical and physical forces. They would say that the carbon atom in natural gas is chemically bonded to hydrogen atoms, with a force of about 100 kcal per mole of hydrogen atoms. At the same time they would say that the hydrocarbon molecules in liquefied natural gas attract one another through physical forces which average less than 1 kcal per mole. Ordinary melting, boiling, and condensation would then be called physical changes and involve the making and breaking of only weak bonds. The evaporation of gasoline would be called a physical change. The energy required is about 7 kcal per mole. Chemical changes, on the other hand, would be defined as those in which strong bonds are broken or formed. The combustion of gasoline in air would be called a chemical change. The energy evolved here is about 1,300 kcal per mole of gasoline.

The supposed distinctions between physical and chemical changes are getting less and less important as we learn more and more about the forces acting between atoms. The nature of the forces acting is quite similar and there is overlap in the energies associated with the various changes. For our purposes the distinction seems to have no advantages and we shall treat interatomic forces in general terms with distinctions based on the strength of the forces rather than whether they might be called chemical or physical.

The Nature of Interatomic Forces

All scientists accept the idea that atoms exist and that they consist of an electrically positive nucleus at their center around which negatively charged electrons move. The details of the electron motions are unknown and are very likely to remain so, but the general distribution of the electron charge about the nucleus is known from many experiments.

Certain numbers of electrons (e.g., those corresponding to the gases helium, neon, argon, krypton, xenon, and radon) can form especially stable electron distributions around nuclei. Many atoms react in such a way that these electron distributions are attained or approximated. Such substances are especially stable. Sodium chloride, quartz, calcium oxide, graphite, are typical examples, as are the gases mentioned above. In fact, until 1962, it was thought that these gases would form no compounds at all since they appeared to have such stable electron configurations.

We need not concern ourselves with the details of chemical bonding. Our concern is with the formation and breaking of these bonds. But it will be helpful to keep in mind that all known attractive forces acting between atoms can be attributed to the simultaneous attraction of one or more electrons by more than one nucleus.

The fact that an atom may contain just enough electrons to balance its total electrical charge exactly at zero does *not* mean that no additional electrons can be attracted by that nucleus. Very seldom is the distribution of electric charge about a nucleus completely spherical. Often the distribution is far from spherical when other atoms are in the vicinity. It is not surprising, then, that electrons "on other atoms" are attracted by the partially exposed nucleus, and that the atoms are drawn toward one another as a result. Of course, as the atoms approach, their electrons (and their nuclei) will mutually repel one another so that a distance will be reached at which the attractive force due to the simultaneous attraction of electrons by more than one nucleus will be balanced by the mutual repulsions of the atomic electrons plus the mutual repulsions of the nuclei. If the kinetic energies of the atoms are sufficiently small, the atoms may remain at this close distance for a long time. We then say a bond has been formed. If the kinetic energies of the atoms become greater, the atoms will separate.

Thus molecules and condensed phases can exist when the kinetic energies of their atoms is sufficiently small. However, if the simultaneous attractions of the electrons by several nuclei are weak compared to the available kinetic energies, separation will occur and the condensed phases or molecules will disintegrate.

A good deal is known about the spatial distribution of the electrons about nuclei and how this spatial distribution affects and reflects the energy of interaction between atoms. Knowledge of these spatial distributions is not required for our purposes. We shall be interested only in changes in the distribution in terms of energy gained or lost, and not in terms of spatial changes.

Molecular Motions

When radiant energy—e.g., ultraviolet light—is passed through gaseous hydrogen chloride, atomic hydrogen and atomic chlorine are formed. The ultraviolet light is absorbed by a hydrogen chloride molecule and converted into kinetic energy of motion. Then the atoms fly apart destroying the molecule. Study of the light absorbed shows that 102 kcal per mole is sufficient to disintegrate hydrogen chloride molecules. This energy can be supplied by light of wave length equal to 2.80×10^{-5} cm or less. (In general, the energy, E, associated with light of wave length λ, is given by, $E = \frac{K}{\lambda}$, where K is a constant.) But the same spectra show that light of other wave lengths and thus other energies is also absorbed. Figure 4.1 is a schematic representation of the complete absorption spectrum of gaseous hydrogen chloride. Other gaseous molecules have similar absorption spectra. In many cases these spectra have been completely analyzed in terms of the molecular changes brought about by the absorption of energy. The theoretical treatment of the absorption process is rather well advanced, and relatively simple equations are known which give results that agree closely with the experimental observations.

For example, in Figure 4.1 we have identified the molecular changes which occur due to the absorption of light of the various energies. Four general types of processes occurring individually or simultaneously are involved: (1) changing the amount of molecular rotation; (2) changing the amount of molecular vibration; (3) changing the electron distribution in the molecule; and (4) changing the nuclear energy. Similar analyses in terms of the same four types of changes are found to be applicable to other substances.

We have already discussed the translational motion (kinetic energy)

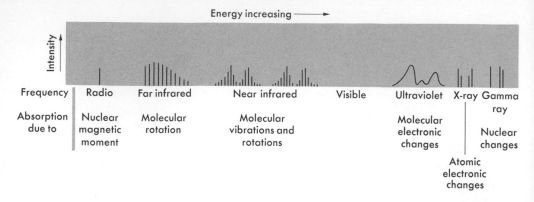

FIGURE *4.1*   *Schematic absorption spectrum of gaseous hydrogen chloride. Notice that, consistent with the colorless nature of the gas, no energy is absorbed in the visible region. But absorption does occur in many other spectral regions due to absorption of energy by the molecule as it undergoes changes in rotational, vibrational, electronic, or nuclear energy content. (Scales are schematic only.)*

of molecules, and the distribution of molecular velocities correlated by the Maxwell-Boltzman theory. We now see that these molecules can also rotate, vibrate, and undergo changes in electron distribution around the nucleus. We shall neglect nuclear changes here.

We also note that only specific and very sharply defined energies are absorbed by the molecule. Thus the molecular energy content can change only by certain well-defined amounts. This intimates that the molecule can hold certain and only certain amounts of energy, and that this energy will be distributed among various rotational, vibrational, and electronic energies.

Molecular Rotations

As shown in Figure 4.1, far infrared energy can be absorbed. The absorbed energy increases the rotational motions of the hydrogen chloride molecule. Figure 4.2 is an enlarged section of the corresponding portion of Figure 4.1. Note that only certain amounts of energy are absorbed; this indicates that only certain levels of rotational energy can be achieved by the molecules. This result is very surprising but is borne out by all known experimental evidence. The regular spacing of the spectral lines can be interpreted in terms of rotational-energy levels spaced as in Figure 4.3. If we call the energy difference between the lowest level (the zero or ground level) and the first level one quantum of rotational energy, we see that the next spacing is two quanta, the next spacing three, etc. We can diagram this as a series of energy steps as shown in Figure 4.3. Thus the total rotational energy of a molecule can be equivalent to 1 quantum of rota-

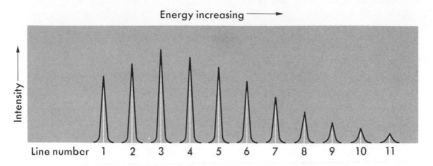

Intensity ⟶

Line number   1   2   3   4   5   6   7   8   9   10   11

FIGURE *4.2   Absorption by gaseous hydrogen chloride in the far infrared region (scales are schematic only). Note the uniform spacing of the lines and the regular gradation in intensities. The absorbed energy is known to change the rotational energy content of the molecule.*

tional energy, 3 quanta, 6 quanta, 10 quanta, etc. But it cannot be equivalent to 2, 4, 5, 7, 8, 9, etc., or any fractional number of quanta.

Why this is so is a question we cannot answer. We observe the spectra which give us information on the actual energy contents of the molecules and we find that these amounts of energy can be contained and other

FIGURE *4.3   Rotational energy level diagram for gaseous hydrogen chloride. The molecule can contain only those amounts of rotational energy represented by the horizontal lines, J = 0, 1, 2, 3, 4, etc. Absorption of energy occurs only when the molecule changes from one amount of rotational energy to the next highest possible amount (or level), △J = +1. The relative energy spacings of the levels—0, 1, 3, 6, 10, 15, 21, 28, etc.— is such that the resulting absorptions of energy (represented by the vertical arrows) differ from one another by a single unit of energy called one quantum of rotational energy. Hence the spectrum consists of a series of equally spaced lines as shown in Figure 4.2.*

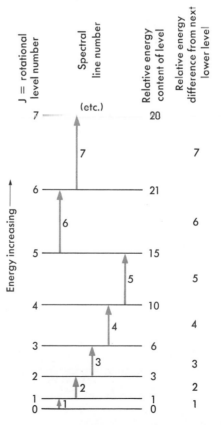

amounts cannot. It is certainly interesting that the observed amounts are so simply related. This makes it easy to remember what they are, and makes it relatively easy to construct mathematical equations and theories which correlate the experimental observations. But none of these advantages constitutes a reason "why" only certain energies can be found within the molecule. They just are that way. (It is interesting to note that we usually treat large objects as able to rotate with any amount of rotational energy. For all practical purposes this is true. However, close study indicates that even here only certain energies are possible. But they are so close to one another that we cannot detect the individual steps.)

Molecular Vibrations

Figure 4.4 shows an enlargement of the portion of the hydrogen chloride spectrum attributed to vibrational changes. A complete analysis shows that these absorptions of energy involve both vibrational and rotational changes. The rotational changes are the same ones we observed previously, which occurred without a change in vibration. We now see that only certain vibrational energies are possible. You are already familiar with the possibility of limited vibrational states in large objects. (Contrast our experience with rotational energies.) After all, one can tune a violin string, drumhead, or bell to emit a certain note no matter how it is struck, and

FIGURE *4.4* *Portion of near infrared absorption spectrum of gaseous hydrogen chloride (schematic). Notice that only certain energies are absorbed. The whole group of absorptions is known as a "band" and is associated with the same change in the vibrational energy of the molecule. The individual absorptions represent different possible simultaneous changes in the rotational energy of the molecule. Thus each absorption causes the same change in the vibrational energy. This change is accompanied by a simultaneous, and varying, change in the rotational energy of the gaseous hydrogen chloride. The interpretation of each of the absorptions shown in Figure 4.4 is indicated in terms of energy levels on the left side of Figure 4.5.*

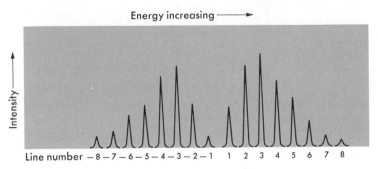

Energy increasing ⟶

Intensity ⟶

Line number − 8 − 7 − 6 − 5 − 4 − 3 − 2 − 1   1   2   3   4   5   6   7   8

all of these sounds are due to the restricted vibrations of the resonant object. One difference between vibrations in large objects and in molecules is the absence of friction in molecules. An undisturbed molecule will vibrate indefinitely. Large objects always tend to convert vibrations into heat.

Another stepwise diagram indicating some possible energy contents of a hydrogen chloride molecule is shown in Figure 4.5. The energy levels associated with the lowest vibrational state are those we have already studied in the rotational changes alone. But now we see that other vibrational energy contents are possible. Again they appear to be simply related to one another. If anything, they are more simply related than were the rotational states, for the vibrational states appear to be equally spaced. If we define the energy difference between the lowest vibrational level and the first level as one quantum of vibrational energy, we see that the second level is one quantum higher in energy, while the third is one more quantum higher. (This simple regularity holds only among the lower vibrational states, as we shall soon see.)

A great deal of evidence is available concerning the vibrations of molecules in general and of hydrogen chloride in particular. If the atoms are vibrating, their internuclear distance must, of course, be continually changing. The vibrational energy will cause the atoms to move toward one another until the mutual electronic and nuclear repulsions stop the motion. The motion will then reverse and the atoms will move apart until the attraction of the electrons by both nuclei causes the motion to reverse again. The over-all vibrational motion is thus determined by the interaction of the fixed amount of vibrational energy, and the mutual attractions and repulsions of the electrons and nuclei. The atoms will continue to move back and forth so long as none of these terms changes.

If energy is absorbed, the amplitude of the vibration will increase since the more energetic atoms can now approach one another more closely against the mutual electron and nuclear repulsions and can also move further apart against the forces attracting the electrons to both nuclei. As more and more vibrational energy is absorbed, the amplitude of motion continues to increase. We find experimentally that the distance of closest approach decreases less rapidly than the distance of farthest extension increases.

Thus the average length of the internuclear distance gets greater and greater as the vibrational energy increases, and increasingly stretches the bond. Eventually the vibrational energy becomes so high that the atoms fly apart and the molecule dissociates. This will happen when the kinetic energy of vibration and the mutual electrical repulsions add together to

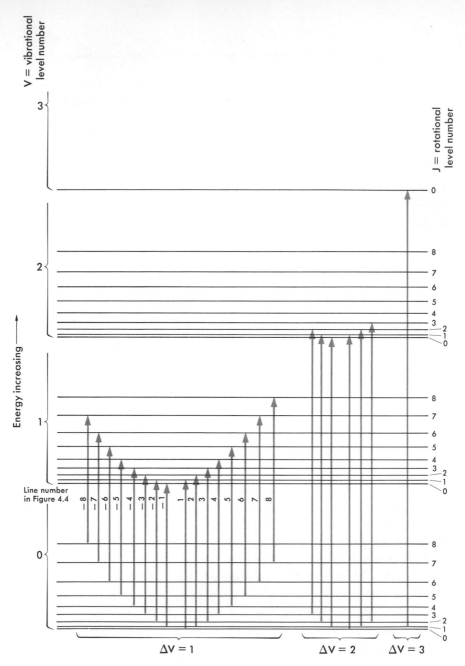

FIGURE *4.5* *Energy-level diagram showing some possible vibrational and rotational energy contents for gaseous hydrogen chloride.
Each of the absorptions shown in Figure 4.4 is represented by a
vertical arrow in the left side of Figure 4.5. The length of the arrow
is proportional to the energy change during the absorption, and each
is numbered to show its correspondence to one of the experimentally
observed absorptions in Figure 4.4. Also indicated are a few of the
absorptions in which the vibrational energy changes by two or three
quanta. Such transitions account for the additional band in the near
infrared indicated in Figure 4.1.*

exceed the force of attraction of the electrons by the two nuclei. If a molecule in the ground state absorbs vibrational energy in excess of this dissociation energy, the molecule will fly apart.

Molecular Potential Energies

This information on the rotational, vibrational, and dissociation energies for hydrogen chloride is summarized as a combined potential-energy diagram in Figure 4.6. The smooth envelope curve indicates

FIGURE 4.6   *Schematic potential-energy diagram for the lowest electronic-energy level of gaseous hydrogen chloride. The smooth envelope curve indicates the variation of the total potential energy of the molecule as the internuclear distance varies. The possible vibrational energies are indicated by the horizontal lines within the envelope. Some of the possible rotational-energy contents are lightly indicated within each of the vibrational levels. Notice that the lower vibrational-energy levels are equally spaced as in Figure 4.5, but come closer together as the total energy increases and the amplitude of vibration increases. At some high value of V (the vibrational quantum number), the vibrational energy exceeds the maximum possible potential energy of attraction of the two atoms for one another and the molecule dissociates (the internuclear distance increases indefinitely).*

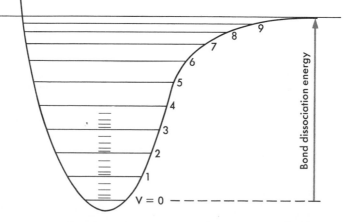

Potential energy increasing →

Bond dissociation energy

V = 0

Internuclear distance increasing →

schematically the extreme distances the atoms reach in their vibrations as a function of the potential energy of the molecule. The heavy horizontal lines indicate schematically some of the observed vibrational energy levels. As the molecule vibrates, its total energy is constant but its potential energy changes with distance, as shown by the smooth envelope curve. The lighter horizontal lines indicate schematically some of the observed rotational energies within some of the vibrational states. This whole figure corresponds to one possible electron distribution in a hydrogen chloride molecule.

As shown in Figure 4.7, similar potential-energy diagrams can be added for other electronic distributions. As with rotations and vibrations, so with electronic energy, only certain energies are observed. Thus only certain potential curves are found, one for each possible electronic distribution. Thus Figure 4.7 shows schematically three possible electronic states for a diatomic molecule such as hydrogen chloride. In each possible electronic distribution, or state, various vibrational energies are observed. And within each vibrational state only certain rotational energies are found. The total potential energy of the molecule is given on the left axis of the diagram and is the sum of the rotational, vibrational, and electronic energy within the molecule.

The total energy of the molecule can then be defined as the sum of the

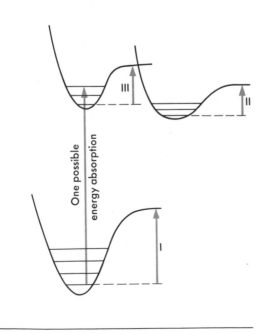

FIGURE *4.7 Schematic total potential-energy diagram. The potential-energy curves for three different electronic states of a diatomic molecule are indicated. The corresponding bond-dissociation energies—I, II, and III—are also indicated. A few of the possible vibrational energies in each electronic state are sketched as horizontal lines. It is transitions between different electronic states such as shown here which account for the absorption of energy by many molecules in the visible and ultraviolet regions of the spectrum. (See Figure 4.1.) During such absorptions, the electronic distribution in the molecule changes and the molecule normally also changes its vibrational and rotational energy content. One possible absorption of energy is indicated by the long vertical arrow in the left of the diagram.*

quantized energies due to rotation, vibration, and electronic distribution and the kinetic energy of the molecule due to its motion through space.

All attracting pairs of atoms which have been studied may be described by potential-energy curves very similar to those of the preceding figures. The curves differ from one pair of atoms to another primarily in the depth of the potential-energy minimum and the value of the average internuclear distance. For a pair of helium atoms, the minimum, you may remember, would be about 0.02 kcal per mole. For nitrogen atoms the minimum would be 225 kcal per mole. More than ten thousand times as much energy is necessary to dissociate two nitrogen atoms from one another as to separate two helium atoms.

Chemical Bond Strengths

Consider a molecule in its lowest vibrational and rotational energy state. The energy which must be absorbed by such a molecule to cause dissociation into two fragments (each also in its lowest electronic, vibrational, and rotational energy state) is called the *bond energy,* or *bond strength.*

The bond strength may be pictured in terms of Figure 4.6 as the energy difference between the lowest energy state and the energy level which first allows dissociation.

At room temperature, most molecules are in their lowest electronic and vibrational state. Therefore, at room temperature the actual dissociation energy is often almost equal to the maximum bond-dissociation energy. At higher temperatures, since the molecules may be vibrating vigorously, the observed dissociation energies may be lower. Thus the bond energy and the dissociation energy are the same only if the reactants and each of the products of the dissociation are in the lowest possible energy states.

This restriction with regard to the products is necessary since the fragments from the dissociation process might have considerable rotational, vibrational, and even electronic energy above their lowest level. More energy is required to dissociate a molecule into fragments containing this extra energy than into fragments in the lowest possible energy states. In fact, one of the biggest experimental difficulties in obtaining values for bond energies is the determination of the "excess" energy in the fragments. It is relatively easy to determine the energy required to break a molecule into pieces, but it is difficult to determine what the energy content is in the pieces obtained.

The strength of a bond does not depend only on the two atoms directly bonded. It also depends on the other atoms in the vicinity. The presently accepted value for the bond dissociation energy of one of the hydrogen-oxygen bonds in an H_2O molecule (to give H and OH) is 118 kcal/mole. The dissociation energy of the hydrogen-oxygen bond in hydroxyl, OH, (to give H and O) is 102 kcal/mole. We know experimentally that the two H—O bonds in H_2O are identical. But clearly the H—O bond in OH has a different bond strength. The equations for these bond-breaking reactions may be written

$$118 \text{ kcal} + H_2O = H + OH \tag{4.1}$$

$$102 \text{ kcal} + OH = H + O \tag{4.2}$$

The total dissociation energy of water into 2H and O must be the sum of these or 220 kcal/mole. Thus the average bond energy in water is 110 kcal per mole, but note there is no bond which can just barely be broken by supplying this average bond energy.

Most tabulated values of bond energies list average values. These averages are useful for estimating the total energy required for complete dissociation of many molecules which have not themselves been studied and even give a general clue to the bond dissociation energies. The value given above of 110 kcal for the average strength of the oxygen-hydrogen bond, for example, agrees within about 10 per cent with the actual bond-dissociation energies which have been measured for O—H bonds. Table 4.2

Table 4.2   SOME BOND DISSOCIATION ENERGIES *

Bond Dissociation energy (kcal/mole)	Li—Li	Na—Na	K—K	F—F	Br—Br	H—Cl	H—Au
	25.8	17.5	11.8	36.8	45.19	102.13	92.0

Bond Dissociation energy (kcal/mole)	H—OH	O—H	H—CH_3	H—C_2H_5	H—$C(CH_3)_3$	H_3C—CH_3	H_3C—$CH_2C_6H_5$
	118	102	101	96	89	83	63

* See also Table 4.1.

lists actual bond-dissociation energies for some common molecules and Table 4.3 lists some average individual bond energies.

It is very important to distinguish between single, double, and triple bonds in discussing bond strengths. Multiple bonds, when they exist be-

Table 4.3 AVERAGE BOND ENERGIES

Bond	C—H	C—C	C=C	C≡C	O—H	C—Cl	C—Br	C—O	C=O	N—H
Energy (kcal/mole)	99	79	141	197	105	76	63	80	169	92

tween any given pair of atoms, always require more energy for breaking than single bonds between the same pair of atoms. Remember, too, that the actual bond-dissociation energies should be used, whenever available, in interpreting chemical reactions. However, the error involved in using the average figure is often less than 10 per cent of the bond energy.

Making Chemical Bonds

Just as the dissociation energy must be absorbed by a molecule before a bond can break, so the recombination of the fragments to produce the original molecule releases a corresponding amount of energy. Thus the dissociation of hydrogen molecules into atoms requires 104 kcal/mole, and the recombination of hydrogen atoms into hydrogen molecules releases 104 kcal/mole. Consider this recombination process on the molecular level in terms of the potential-energy diagram in Figure 4.8.

As the two hydrogen atoms approach each other, they will begin to attract each other and accelerate toward each other. Their kinetic energy of motion along the internuclear axis will rise as the velocity increases because of the increasing attraction as they come closer together. This

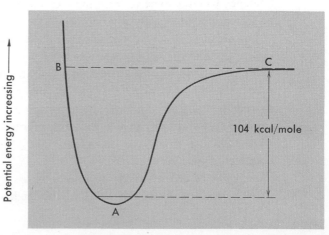

FIGURE *4.8* *Potential-energy diagram for the lowest electronic-energy level of gaseous molecular hydrogen. The lowest vibrational state is indicated and the bond-dissociation energy of 104 kcal/mole is shown.*

104 kcal/mole

Potential energy increasing →

Internuclear distance increasing →

attraction, of course, is due to the fact that at these smaller distances the electrons are attracted simultaneously to both nuclei and the resulting forces tend to draw the atoms together. At distances smaller than that represented by the minimum, *A,* in the potential-energy curve, the mutual repulsions between the two nuclei and between the two electrons begin to become important. The motion of the particles toward each other begins to slow as the internuclear distance decreases. The kinetic energies of the particles begins to decrease and the potential energy begins to rise. At some small distance, *B,* the repulsive forces bring the two atoms momentarily to rest with respect to each other. But at this small distance the net electrical repulsions in the system are now considerably greater than the electrical attractive forces. The atoms begin to move apart as though undergoing a vibration. As they "fall down" the potential-energy curve they accelerate until they reach the distance, *A,* corresponding to the potential-energy minimum. Then they begin to "rise up" the other side of the potential-energy curve. Their relative velocity decreases. But as they approach the top of this curve, the curve flattens (unlike the potential curve at small distances which got steeper and steeper). The atoms have just enough energy to reach the top of this curve, *C,* which was where they started, but there is now no force tending to bring them back together so they keep on separating and fly apart.

The two atoms cannot form a molecule since there is no way for them to get rid of the energy generated by the formation of the bond. Since the energy generated as the bond formed is exactly the same as the energy necessary to dissociate the bond, the atoms fly apart after one vibration. As a result, atomic hydrogen is a relatively stable substance with respect to formation of hydrogen molecules. The use of atomic hydrogen in high-temperature cutting torches is based on the fact that the atoms have little tendency to recombine to form the molecules. Yet atomic hydrogen cannot be stored indefinitely. By what process does it recombine?

Our detailed discussion of the collision between two atoms of hydrogen indicated that the atoms remained "in contact" for the length of one vibration. If, during this period, the pair of atoms struck a third object, such as another atom or the wall of the container, some of the energy shared by the pair of atoms might be transferred to the third object. If some energy were lost in this way, the rebounding atoms would no longer have sufficient energy to dissociate. They would remain together as a hydrogen molecule.

Transfer of energy to the surroundings is especially rapid in condensed phases—solids and liquids—due to the high rate of molecular collisions there. Only in gases does one experimentally find it difficult to get rid of the energy of bond formation.

The description above applies in general to the formation of any chemical bond. The bond can form and be stable only if some method is available for losing to the surroundings at least part of the energy of formation of the bond. Otherwise the fragments which have collided will again fly apart since they contain too much kinetic energy to remain together.

Complicated molecules need not always lose the energy of bond formation to other molecules. They can sometimes absorb it in other internal motions of the complicated molecule. For example, some of the energy generated as the fragments approach one another may be used in causing additional vibrations or rotations of the molecule. This removes energy from the region of the bond which is forming and makes it impossible for the fragments to dissociate from one another as they rebound.

Bond Strengths and Activation Energies

Based on the previous discussion, one might be justified in assuming that chemical reactions occur when molecules collide in an appropriate orientation and with sufficient activation energy to break bonds. The resulting fragments might then separate and later combine with other fragments to give the final products. In this case the activation energies should correspond to the bond-dissociation energies of the fragmented bond. Table 4.4 compares bond-dissociation energies and activation energies for a few simple net reactions. Even superficial examination shows that there is no general correlation between bond-dissociation energies and experimentally observed activation energies. In most cases the activa-

Table 4.4 COMPARISON OF BOND STRENGTHS AND ACTIVATION ENERGIES FOR SOME SIMPLE REACTIONS

Reaction	Activation Energy (kcal/mole)	Bond Strengths (kcal/mole)
$H_2 + Cl_2 \rightarrow 2\,HCl$ (photochemical)	60 *	$H_2 = 104,\, Cl_2 = 58$
$2\,HI \rightarrow H_2 + I_2$	44	$HI = 72$
$2\,NO + Br_2 \rightarrow 2NOBr$	1.3	$NO = 147,\, Br_2 = 45$
$CN^- + CH_3I \rightarrow CH_3CN + I^-$	20	$CH_3-I = 47$

* Minimum energy per quantum which will initiate the reaction.

tion energy is somewhat smaller than the bond-dissociation energy of the weakest bond in any of the reactants. Examination of all available data shows that this is true for the great majority of reactions.

In one case in Table 4.4, the activation energy is almost the same as the dissociation energy of a bond in one of the reactants. The activation energy for the photochemical gas-phase reaction between hydrogen and chlorine is 60 kcal/mole and the minimum bond-dissociation energy of chlorine into chlorine atoms is 58 kcal/mole. This indicates that the rate-determining step in the reaction mechanism is probably the dissociation of chlorine molecules. All other available data on this reaction corroborate this.

But why is it that the activation energy is usually less than the bond-dissociation energy of either reactant? It should be clear from our discussion of energetics and reaction rates that the reaction will go faster, other things being equal, if only a small activation energy is required. For any given reaction there is a very large number of possible mechanisms, but the one having the lowest activation energy will usually be the fastest. If a mechanism exists which requires less energy than the breaking of a bond, this lower-energy mechanism will occur more often than that requiring the bond to break. If the difference in energy requirement is sufficient we will be able to detect only the faster mechanism with our analytical tools, even though the other mechanism may be proceeding to a limited extent.

In the hydrogen iodide case a bimolecular collision leads to the formation of an intermediate molecule, H_2I_2. In this molecule the hydrogen-iodine bonds are longer, and therefore weaker, than in the hydrogen iodide molecules. But at the same time bonds have formed between the two hydrogens and between the two iodines. These bonds are weaker than those in hydrogen or iodine molecules, but their formation has liberated some energy since the electrons are now attracted by both hydrogen and both iodine nuclei. The weakening of the hydrogen iodide bonds required energy, though not as much as would be required to break the bonds completely. The formation of the new hydrogen and iodine bonds liberated energy. The activation energy is the difference between these two terms and is, as might be expected, considerably less than the bond dissociation energies.

Most chemical reactions proceed by mechanisms which involve intermediate molecules. In these molecules new bonds begin to form even as the old bonds are breaking. The net effect is to lower the activation energy compared to that required to break fully the old bonds. Thus mechanisms in which intermediate molecules form tend to be more rapid than mechanisms requiring complete molecular fragmentation.

In photochemical reactions, however, molecular fragmentation is a very common mechanistic step. The decomposition of Cl_2 into 2 Cl is what initiates the photochemical reaction between H_2 and Cl_2. Photochemical reactions are reactions that require the absorption of radiant energy. The absorbed radiant energy often accomplishes bond dissociation. As a result much of the data on bond-dissociation energies come from photochemical studies. We have already mentioned the photochemical dissociation of hydrogen chloride when ultraviolet light is absorbed.

Photochemical reactions are similar to reactions resulting from molecular collisions in that a collision between a molecule and a photon of radiant energy is required. The photon must have sufficient energy to activate the molecule, and, in many cases, there is even a geometrical requirement for the relative orientation of the molecule before the photon can be absorbed. If we treat a photon as a molecule of radiant energy the parallelism is quite complete.

Reaction-Energy Diagrams

A common way of pictorially presenting the energetics of a reaction is through a reaction-energy diagram. Let us consider the hydrogen-iodine case since the mechanism is so simple and the data are readily available. The over-all equation is

$$H_{2(g)} + I_{2(g)} = 2 \, HI_{(g)} + 4 \text{ kcal} \qquad (4.3)$$

Thus the potential energy of two moles of hydrogen iodide is 4 kcal less than the potential energy of one mole of hydrogen plus the potential energy of one mole of iodine. This change in potential energy appears as the energy released during the reaction. Figure 4.9 represents this potential-energy change diagrammatically. If it had been necessary to dissociate completely the elements into their atoms before reaction could occur, the activation energy would have corresponded to the sum of the bond energy in hydrogen (103 kcal/mole) plus that in iodine (36 kcal/mole). Thus 139 kcal of activation energy would have been required per mole of hydrogen reacting. When these atoms recombine to give hydrogen iodide, enough energy would be released to take the atoms from the activated state to the final energy state of hydrogen iodide. Figure 4.9 shows that this energy release would equal the sum of the activation energy to give the atoms (139 kcal/mole) and the energy of the over-all reaction (4 kcal/mole), or a total of 143 kcal. Actually the activation energy is far less than 139 kcal. It is 40 kcal per mole of hydrogen reacting. Thus the energy released (44 kcal/mole) when the intermediate molecule decomposes into two moles of hydrogen iodide is also less than would have been released had the mechanism been accomplished through the recombination of atomic hydrogen and atomic iodine. But the over-all energy of reaction (4 kcal/mole) is independent of the mechanism. The over-all energy depends only on the

FIGURE 4.9   Reaction-energy diagram for the reaction, $H_2 + I_2 =$ 2 HI. The activation energy, $\triangle E$, assuming complete dissociation of the reactants into atoms 2 H and 2 I, is shown for the forward (I) and reverse (IV) reaction. The experimentally observed activation energies for the forward (II) and reverse (III) reactions are indicated. The lower values of II and III compared to I and IV are interpreted in terms of the formation of an intermediate molecule, H_2I_2. The over-all energy change, $\triangle E$, is also indicated (V). Note that $\triangle E$ is independent of the reaction mechanism. Either I-IV or II-III equals V. The same would be true for any other set of activation energies. In general, $\triangle E = \triangle E^{\ddagger}_{forward} - \triangle E^{\ddagger}_{reverse}$. (Remember that values of activation energies are always positive.)

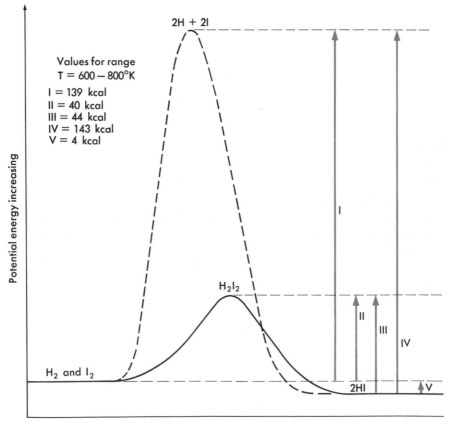

Values for range
T = 600 − 800°K
I = 139 kcal
II = 40 kcal
III = 44 kcal
IV = 143 kcal
V = 4 kcal

initial and final states of the reactants and products, and is always 4 kcal/mole for this reaction, regardless of the mechanism.

Reaction-energy diagrams similar to Figure 4.9 can be sketched for any reaction for which the over-all energy change and the activation energy are known.

The "reaction coordinate" used as the abscissa in a reaction-energy diagram is actually a complicated function of interatomic distances. For all practical purposes, however, the reaction coordinate for simple molecules can be considered as representing the changes in distances which occur as the reactants approach one another to form the activated complex and as the activated complex disintegrates into the products. The vertical potential-energy coordinate represents the total potential energy of the system as these changes in distance occur.

It is wise to remember that each reaction-energy diagram corresponds to some particular orientation in the activated complex. The reaction diagram which corresponds to the experimentally observed activation energy corresponds to the most favorable orientation for reaction. Reaction diagrams for less favorable orientations would have higher activation energies and would represent slower rates.

Catalysts

We found in our study of the methylene blue reaction that it is quite possible to have substances react in the rate-determining step; substances which are regenerated and thus not permanently consumed in the reaction. Substances which affect the rate of a chemical reaction, but are not permanently consumed (i.e., their concentration does not change as a result of the reaction) are called *catalysts*.

Catalysts increase reaction rates by providing a new mechanism for the reaction. The reaction can, of course, still proceed by the old mechanism. The fact that a catalyst provides an additional mechanism means that the total rate is bound to be faster. In fact, most catalysts provide a new mechanism which is itself much faster than the old one. Thus the total rate is considerably increased. "Good catalysts" are those causing the greatest changes in rate. The catalytic mechanism may be fast because it eases the orientation requirement, or because the new mechanism requires a lower activation energy, or both. Actually, in most cases the activation energy for the catalyzed reaction is, indeed, low. The methylene blue, the hydroxide ions, and the water were all catalysts in the oxidation of glucose studied in Chapter 2.

Substances are also known which decrease the rate of reactions. These are sometimes called negative catalysts, a rather unfortunate term as generally used. Substances which slow reactions do so by reacting with some intermediate essential to the reaction mechanism. If the added substance reacts very rapidly with this intermediate, the intermediate is removed and the original mechanism is essentially stopped. The most common mechanism for the action of these substances involves their combination with free radicals (i.e., molecules containing unpaired electrons) which are required in some chain reactions. Alternatively, negative catalysts may combine with active sites on a molecule or surface and thus prevent reaction there. The use of acetanilide to "preserve" commercial hydrogen peroxide is based on the fact that the acetanilide can rapidly destroy the free radicals that are important catalysts for the decomposition of the peroxide. The "poisoning" of platinum catalysts used in the oxidation of sulfur dioxide to sulfur trioxide results when traces of substances (such as arsenic) cover the reactive sites on the platinum catalyst. The addition of carbon monoxide will hinder the catalytic action of methylene blue, and the addition of acids will lower catalysis due to hydroxide ions. A layer of paint acts as a "negative catalyst" for the rotting of wood.

Questions

1. Most people have observed that the damp air in a basement or cave seems cooler than the drier air outside. Yet a thermometer may show that the temperature is the same in both places. Account for this apparent cooling effect of cool, moist air. (Note that if the air temperature is above body temperature, $37°C$, the effect reverses—i.e., moist air then feels hotter.)
2. Designing rockets requires a knowledge of the temperature of the exit gases after combustion. Designs based on early calculations produced rockets which did not perform satisfactorily. The actual exhaust temperatures were considerably below the calculated ones. What energy-absorbing processes occur in rocket flames at several thousand degrees Kelvin that are not common in the laboratory calorimeters used to measure heats of reactions?
3. Gasoline cracking plants have appreciable concentrations of gaseous H, CH_3, and C_2H_5 present in the reactor chambers. Discuss the factors which will affect the relative rates of the four reactions shown below. What is the most likely product between pairs of these reactants? Which is the least likely? Assume that all are initially present in comparable concentrations.

$$H + H \rightarrow H_2$$
$$H + CH_3 \rightarrow CH_4$$
$$H + C_2H_5 \rightarrow C_2H_6$$
$$CH_3 + C_2H_5 \rightarrow C_3H_8$$

4. Hydrogen ions are one of the most common and most effective catalysts in reactions in aqueous systems. Suggest some reasons for this.

5. Draw a typical reaction coordinate-potential energy curve. What feature represented on the curve helps determine the rate of the reaction? How would the rate be changed if the potential energy of the products were lowered? If the potential energy of the intermediate molecule were lowered? If the potential energy of the reactants were lowered? How might we try to accomplish each of these changes experimentally?

5

Rate and Equilibrium

Thus far we have distinguished between reactants and products in our discussion. Now let us discuss just how fundamental this distinction really is.

Reversible (and Irreversible) Reactions

The curve drawn in Figure 4.9 illustrates a typical relationship between the potential energy and the path of reaction, or reaction coordinate, in a chemical system. Let's use it again to re-examine the hydrogen-iodine system.

Hydrogen and iodine molecules will continually collide randomly in a mixture of the two gases. When a collision has an appropriate orientation and involves sufficient activation energy, the chemical bonds may rearrange to form the intermediate molecule. Further bond rearrangement lets the intermediate molecule decompose into two molecules of hydrogen iodide.

But the hydrogen iodide molecules will also engage in random collision with the hydrogen molecules, with iodine molecules, and with one another. And if they collide with one another in a suitable orientation and with sufficient energy there seems to be no reason why they might not reform the intermediate molecule, which might this time decompose into molecular hydrogen and molecular iodine. If so, the reaction would have reversed itself.

Table 5.1   SOME EQUILIBRIUM DATA
ON THE H_2, I_2, HI SYSTEM
AT 698.6°K (CONCENTRATIONS IN MOLES/LITER)

	Initial Concentrations			Final Concentrations		
Expt.	H_2	I_2	III	H_2	I_2	III
1	10.6673×10^{-3}	11.9652×10^{-3}	0	1.8313×10^{-3}	3.1292×10^{-3}	17.671×10^{-3}
2	10.6673×10^{-3}	10.7610×10^{-3}	0	2.2423×10^{-3}	2.3360×10^{-3}	16.850×10^{-3}
3	11.3540×10^{-3}	9.0440×10^{-3}	0	3.5600×10^{-3}	1.2500×10^{-3}	15.588×10^{-3}
4	8.6737×10^{-3}	4.8468×10^{-3}	5.326×10^{-3}	4.5647×10^{-3}	0.7378×10^{-3}	13.544×10^{-3}
5	0	0	10.692×10^{-3}	1.1409×10^{-3}	1.1409×10^{-3}	8.410×10^{-3}
6	0	0	4.646×10^{-3}	0.4953×10^{-3}	0.4953×10^{-3}	3.655×10^{-3}

Table 5.1 lists some experimental evidence supporting the idea that this reversal actually does occur. Various flasks, some initially containing hydrogen and iodine, some initially containing only hydrogen iodide, and one initially containing all three substances, all prove to contain all three substances after they have been allowed to stand for some time at the same temperature and have come to equilibrium. Not only can hydrogen and iodine react to form hydrogen iodide; hydrogen iodide can also react with itself to form hydrogen and iodine.

Our intuitive suggestion that the random collisions characteristic of molecules should lead to the reversal of reactions is consistent with the experimental findings. The intuitive idea is perfectly general; it should apply to any system. The experiments can be done successfully only when the amount of each substance in the container is sufficient to be detected by available analytical tools. However, the experimental evidence is overwhelming that all chemical reactions really are reversible. In some cases reaction may proceed so far in one direction that it is impossible to detect any of the original reactants with available techniques. But past experience indicates that more refined measurements would show that some of the original reactants are present.

We shall supply further experimental evidence later but merely state here that, if none of the products of a reaction are allowed to escape from the reaction vessel, any chemical reaction is reversible. Of course, if one or more of the products are removed, collision with them becomes impossible, and the reverse reaction can no longer occur.

The Equilibrium State

The concept of the reversibility of chemical reactions leads to some interesting conclusions as to the state a chemical reaction will reach given sufficient time.

Consider the hydrogen-iodine system once more. If one starts with hydrogen and iodine, only collisions among these molecules can occur. Collision of hydrogen with hydrogen may result in exchange of partners, and the same thing may happen when two iodine molecules collide. In these cases there would be no net reaction. (Can you suggest, however, an experiment that would show whether such exchanges actually occur or not? We will discuss such a method shortly.)

When hydrogen and iodine molecules collide with a suitable orientation and sufficient activation energy, hydrogen iodide can be produced. Initially only a few hydrogen iodide molecules are produced. But their concentration will increase with time. If these hydrogen iodide molecules collide with hydrogen or iodine molecules, partner exchange may (in fact does) occur again, but there is no net change in the kinds of molecules present. However, as the concentration of hydrogen iodide rises, it becomes more and more likely that two hydrogen iodide molecules will collide. Given the proper orientation and activation energy they may form the activated complex and thus reform hydrogen and iodine. The likelihood of this reverse reaction will rise as the concentration of the hydrogen iodide rises. On the other hand, the likelihood of hydrogen molecules meeting iodine molecules to form hydrogen iodide will decrease as more and more of the elements are used up in forming hydrogen iodide. Thus the rate of formation of hydrogen iodide will decrease with time whereas the rate of reaction of hydrogen iodide with itself will increase.

At some set of concentrations the rate of successful collisions between hydrogen and iodine should have fallen until it just equals the rising rate at which hydrogen iodide is reacting with itself. When the rates of these two reactions—the forward reaction and the reverse reaction—become equal, no further net changes will occur. Hydrogen iodide will form and react at the same rate as hydrogen and iodine; all concentrations will become constant as a function of time. Thus the system will have reached equilibrium. But since all the reactions are still occurring, the system is said at to be at *dynamic equilibrium*.

A schematic representation of the change in concentration with time is shown in Figure 5.1, assuming that the only reaction is $H_2 + I_2 = 2\,HI$.

The concentrations of hydrogen and iodine need not be equal at the beginning of the reaction, but the two concentrations will decrease at the same rate. This rate of decrease will diminish with time since fewer and fewer collisions occur as the concentrations drop. The concentration of hydrogen iodide will rise at twice this rate since two moles are produced per mole of hydrogen (or iodine) that reacts. This rate of increase of (HI) will also be rapid at first and then slower as less is produced per unit of time, and as the hydrogen iodide begins to react with itself to produce hydrogen and iodine. At equilibrium all of the concentrations become constant and their rates of change become zero.

The dynamic nature of this equilibrium may be demonstrated experi-

FIGURE 5.1   *The concentrations of hydrogen, iodine, and hydrogen iodide as a function of time (data from Experiment 3, Table 5.1). Initially there is a net reaction, $H_2 + I_2 \rightarrow 2\,HI$, during which the concentrations of hydrogen and iodine decrease at equal rates while the concentration of hydrogen iodide increases at twice this rate. Finally an equilibrium state is reached in which the concentrations of all three substances become constant since the forward and reverse reactions are proceeding at equal rates and in opposite directions.*

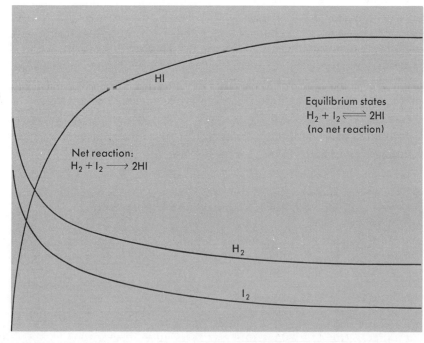

Concentration increasing ⟶

HI

Equilibrium states
$H_2 + I_2 \rightleftharpoons 2HI$
(no net reaction)

Net reaction:
$H_2 + I_2 \longrightarrow 2HI$

H_2

I_2

Time increasing ⟶

mentally by allowing equilibrium to be reached and then introducing a small amount of radioactive elementary iodine or hydrogen. Very quickly thereafter it will be possible to detect radioactivity in the hydrogen iodide. Or hydrogen iodide containing radioactive hydrogen or iodine may be introduced. In this case the elementary hydrogen and iodine in the flask will quickly prove to contain radioactive atoms. Measurement of the rate proves the reactions are between H_2 and I_2 and between HI and HI.

This last experiment is particularly easy to perform since iodine and hydrogen iodide solidify much more easily than does hydrogen. The system is allowed to come to equilibrium. Hydrogen iodide, containing radioactive hydrogen, is then introduced. The resulting mixture is passed through a liquid-air trap freezing the iodine and hydrogen iodide. The hydrogen gas which remains proves to be radioactive, showing that the equilibrium was a dynamic one.

All experiments that have been performed indicate that chemical equilibria are dynamic. Chemical equilibria always involve states which do not change with time, but states in which each possible reaction and its reverse are continually occurring at equal rates. Individual atoms and molecules continue to react, but the system as a whole does not undergo net change.

An Empirical Observation

The equilibrium data in Table 5.2 (repeated from Table 5.1) have considerable regularity to them. When the equilibrium concentration of hydrogen iodide remains about the same (Expts. 1, 2, and 3), an increase in the hydrogen concentration (Col. I) is accompanied by a decrease in that of iodine (Col. II). Similarly (Expts. 5 and 6), if the hydrogen iodide equilibrium concentration decreases (Col. III), the concentrations of both hydrogen and iodine (Cols. I and II) also decrease.

Table 5.2 EMPIRICAL EXPLORATION OF THE EQUILIBRIUM DATA FOR H_2, I_2, HI AT $698.6°K$ (EQUILIBRIUM CONCENTRATIONS IN MOLES/LITER)

	I	II	III	IV $\dfrac{(H_2)(I_2)}{(HI)}$	V $\dfrac{(H_2)(I_2)}{(HI)^2}$
Expt.	(H_2)	(I_2)	(HI)		
1	1.8313×10^{-3}	3.1292×10^{-3}	17.671×10^{-3}	3.25×10^{-4}	1.835×10^{-2}
2	2.2423×10^{-3}	2.3360×10^{-3}	16.850×10^{-3}	3.11×10^{-4}	1.853×10^{-2}
3	3.5600×10^{-3}	1.2500×10^{-3}	15.588×10^{-3}	2.86×10^{-4}	1.831×10^{-2}
4	4.5647×10^{-3}	0.7378×10^{-3}	13.544×10^{-3}	2.49×10^{-4}	1.835×10^{-2}
5	1.1409×10^{-3}	1.1409×10^{-3}	8.410×10^{-3}	1.55×10^{-4}	1.840×10^{-2}
6	0.4953×10^{-3}	0.4953×10^{-3}	3.655×10^{-3}	6.70×10^{-5}	1.832×10^{-2}

When such regularities are observed we usually try to find a mathematical formula that will correlate the regularities. We notice that the concentrations of hydrogen and iodine seem inversely related, but both appear directly related to hydrogen iodide. What happens if we substitute the data in the simple relation, $\frac{(H_2)\,(I_2)}{(HI)}$, as in Table 5.2, Col. IV, where the quantities in parenthesis represent the concentrations in moles/liter of the respective gases. The quotient has a regular trend, decreasing as (HI) decreases. Suppose we divide each of these quotients by (HI), that is, we calculate $\frac{(H_2)\,(I_2)}{(HI)^2}$ as in the last column (V) of Table 5.2. A marked regularity now occurs: all the quotients are constant.

Such a constant quotient of the concentrations can always be written for every system at chemical equilibrium. This was discovered empirically about 100 years ago, originally was doubted, and then proved true by careful experimental work. Its full theoretical interpretation waited till the second decade of the 20th century and its ramifications are still being explored. Let's see why such a constant quotient always exists.

Microscopic Reversibility

If we consider a general case in which there may be many mechanistic steps, rather than merely a simple case like hydrogen-iodine where only one step is involved in the mechanism, we must consider more reactions. Let us use the methylene blue example. (Remember: MeBl represents methylene blue; GlOH represents glucose.) The mechanism finally proposed was

$$O_{2(g)} \to O_{2(aq)} \tag{5.1}$$

$$\underset{\text{colorless}}{O_2} + \underset{\text{blue}}{MeBl} \to MeBl \text{ (all aqueous)} \tag{5.2}$$

$$GlOH + OH^- \rightleftharpoons GlO^- + H_2O \text{ (all aqueous)} \tag{5.3}$$

$$\underset{\text{blue}}{MeBl} + \underset{\text{colorless}}{GlO^-} \to \underset{\text{colorless}}{MeBl} + OH^- + \text{products (all aqueous)} \tag{5.4}$$

The use of arrows indicates that, in our discussion of the mechanism, we were interested only in the pathway by which the products were formed. Eventually, however, this system, like all systems in closed containers, would come to equilibrium. Initially the concentrations of oxygen and glucose would diminish, making it less likely that they would undergo collision and react. The concentrations of the products would rise, increasing the rate of the reverse reaction. Finally equilibrium would be reached. At equilibrium each of the reactions above would proceed in both directions, a fact we can explicitly indicate by the use of double arrows (as in equation 5.3 above) for the equilibrium state. The idea that each mechanistic step must be at equilibrium when the whole system is at equilibrium is known as the *principle of microscopic reversibility*.

$$O_{2(g)} \underset{6}{\overset{5}{\rightleftharpoons}} O_{2(aq)} \qquad (5.5, 6)$$

$$O_2 + \underset{\text{colorless}}{\text{MeBl}} \underset{8}{\overset{7}{\rightleftharpoons}} \underset{\text{blue}}{\text{MeBl}} \text{ (all aqueous)} \qquad (5.7, 8)$$

$$\text{GlOH} + \text{OH}^- \underset{10}{\overset{9}{\rightleftharpoons}} \text{GlO}^- + H_2O \text{ (all aqueous)} \qquad (5.9, 10)$$

$$\underset{\text{blue}}{\text{GlO}^-} + \text{MeBl} \underset{12}{\overset{11}{\rightleftharpoons}} \underset{\text{colorless}}{\text{MeBl}} + \text{OH}^- + \underset{\text{colorless}}{\text{products}} \text{ (all aqueous)} \qquad (5.11, 12)$$

$$\textit{Net: } O_{2(g)} + \text{GlOH}_{(aq)} \underset{14}{\overset{13}{\rightleftharpoons}} \underset{\text{colorless}}{\text{products}_{(aq)}} \qquad (5.13, 14)$$

Thus, indirectly, the products must be in equilibrium with the reactants.

We have shown that the rate of any actual mechanistic step may be written in the form (see equation 3.2)

$$\text{rate} = k \times \text{(function of the concentrations of reactants)} \qquad (5.15)$$

In any actual mechanistic step, we know from the facts that collisions are necessary to give reaction and that the collision rate depends on the numerical product of the concentrations of the reactants, that the quantity (function of the concentration of the reactants), merely equals the product of their concentrations.

Consider, for example, reactions 9 and 10. For reaction 9:

$$\text{(rate of reaction)}_9 = k_9 \text{ (GlOH) (OH}^-) \qquad (5.16)$$

where the sub 9's merely refer to reaction 9. For reaction 10:

$$\text{(rate of reaction)}_{10} = k_{10} \text{ (GlO}^-) (H_2O)$$

At equilibrium the rates of these two opposite reactions become equal, so

$$\text{(rate of reaction)}_9 = \text{(rate of reaction)}_{10} \qquad (5.17)$$

$$k_9 \text{ (GlOH) (OH}^-) = k_{10} \text{ (GlO}^-) (H_2O) \qquad (5.18)$$

We can now take equation 5.18 involving the k's and collect the k's on one side and the concentration terms on the other. Then:

$$\frac{k_9}{k_{10}} = \frac{(GlO^-)\,(H_2O)}{(GlOH)\,(OH^-)} = k'_{9,10} \qquad (5.19)$$

Since the ratio of k_9 to k_{10} is itself a constant, we can call this ratio $k'_{9,10}$. Since the concentration of water is very large in aqueous solutions and, thus, does not change appreciably during a reaction we can treat (H_2O) as a constant. We can then write

$$\frac{(GlO^-)}{(GlOH)\,(OH^-)} = \frac{k'_{9,10}}{(H_2O)} = K_{9,10} \qquad (5.20)$$

$K_{9,10}$ is called the equilibrium constant for the dynamic equilibrium reaction between glucose, hydroxide ion, and glucoside ion in water.

We could go through the same extended derivation for the equilibria in each of the steps. It should suffice to say, however, that it is always possible to write an equilibrium constant for any actual step at equilibrium. And, following the type of derivation used above, we can show that this equilibrium-constant expression is always of the type in which the equilibrium constant, K, is equal to the ratio of the product of the concentrations of the materials on the right side of the equation, divided by the product of the concentrations of the reactants on the left side of the equation (each concentration raised to a power equal to the coefficient of that species in the chemical equation).

Simple inspection of equations 5–6, 7–8, 9–10, and 11–12 allows us to write the following equilibrium-constant expressions:

$$K_{5,6} = \frac{(O_{2(aq)})}{(O_{2(g)})} \ (5.21); \qquad K_{7,8} = \frac{(MeBl\text{-}blue)}{(O_{2(aq)})\,(MeBl\text{-}colorless)} \ (5.22)$$

$$K_{9,10} = \frac{(GlO^-)}{(GlOH)\,(OH^-)} \qquad (5.23)$$

$$K_{11,12} = \frac{(MeBl\text{-}colorless)\,(OH^-)\,(products)}{(GlO^-)\,(MeBl\text{-}blue)} \qquad (5.24)$$

An interesting and very useful result is obtained if we multiply these four equations together. We do this by multiplying all the left-hand terms, $K_{5,6}$, $K_{7,8}$, $K_{9,10}$, $K_{11,12}$, together to give a new constant, K_{5-12}.

$$K_{5,6} \times K_{7,8} \times K_{9,10} \times K_{11,12} = K_{5-12} \qquad (5.25)$$

$$K_{5-12} = \frac{(O_{2(aq)})}{(O_{2(g)})} \times \frac{(MeBl\text{-}blue)}{(O_{2(aq)})\,(MeBl\text{-}colorless)} \times \frac{(GlO^-)}{(GlOH)\,(OH^-)} \times$$

$$\frac{(MeBl\text{-}colorless)\,(OH^-)\,(products)}{(GlO^-)\,(MeBl\text{-}blue)} \qquad (5.26)$$

But this cumbersome equation contains many terms on the right which are identical in the numerator and denominator. If we cancel such terms we obtain

$$K_{5\text{-}12} = \frac{(\text{products})}{(O_{2(g)})\,(GlOH)} \tag{5.27}$$

Comparing this with the equation for the net reaction

$$O_{2(g)} + GlOH = \text{products} \tag{5.28}$$

shows that the concentrations of all the reactants and final products appear in the expression for the constant $K_{5\text{-}12}$ and that no other concentrations affect this constant. This remarkably useful conclusion is perfectly general. One can start with the chemical equation for the net reaction for any system at equilibrium and write down a function of the concentrations which will always be constant at any given temperature. The numerical value of the constant, symbolized by K or K_{eq}, may be obtained by determining the concentrations of all the reactants and products at equilibrium (any set of equilibrium concentrations will do) and substituting their numerical values in the algebraic expression. The resulting numerical equilibrium constant can then be used to predict other possible sets of concentrations that could exist at equilibrium. In fact, any set of concentrations which satisfies the expression is a possible set of equilibrium concentrations. Conversely, any set of concentrations which does not satisfy the algebraic expression represents a nonequilibrium state of the system.

Table 5.3 gives the equilibrium-constant expressions for several other net reactions. Notice that the equilibrium-constant expression can be written by simple examination of the chemical equation for the net reaction. It is not necessary to go through the mechanistic approach. One merely places the product of the concentrations of the products (each raised to a power identical to its coefficient in the net equation) in the numerator and the product of the concentrations of the reactants (again raised to appropriate powers) in the denominator. The resulting quotient is the equilibrium constant, K, for that net reaction.

The proof of the existence of the equilibrium-constant expression may be reached in many ways. Using experimental data, we have shown empirically that such a function existed for the hydrogen-iodine reaction. We then used the principle of microscopic reversibility to generalize. Other

Table 5.3   SOME EQUILIBRIUM-CONSTANT EXPRESSIONS

Equilibrium Reaction	*Equilibrium-Constant Expression*
$H_2 + I_2 = 2\,HI$	$K = (HI)^2/(H_2)(I_2)$; note $(HI)^2$ since 2 HI in equation.
$GlOH + OH^- = GlO^- + H_2O$	$K = (GlO^-)/(GlOH)(OH^-)$; note (H_2O) is included in K since concentration in liquid is constant.
$Cl_2 + C_2H_4 = C_2H_4Cl_2$	$K = (C_2H_4Cl_2)/(Cl_2)(C_2H_4)$.
$2\,H_2 + O_2 = 2\,H_2O$ (all gases)	$K = (H_2O)^2/(H_2)^2(O_2)$, note (H_2O) retained since concentration in gas can vary.
$3\,Fe_{(s)} + 4\,H_2O_{(g)} = Fe_3O_{4(s)} + 4\,H_{2(g)}$	$K = (H_2)^4/(H_2O)^4$; note concentrations of $Fe_{(s)}$ and $Fe_3O_{4(s)}$ are included in K, since the concentration of a pure solid is constant at constant temperature.
$2\,A + 3\,B = 4\,D + E$	$K = (D)^4(E)/(A)^2(B)^3$; a general example.

methods are possible. Since so many independent pieces of evidence indicate the existence of an equilibrium constant for every reaction, we are further confirmed in our belief that chemical equilibria are dynamic and reversible if the system is given sufficient time.

The Equilibrium State and Concentration

The equilibrium-constant expression for any reaction gives the algebraic relationship between the concentrations of the various species participating in the equilibrium. In general, changing the concentration of any one of the species in the reacting mix will upset the dynamic equilibrium. Reactions involving a species whose concentration is increased should become more likely, since its collision rate has been increased. Thus the rates of reactions involving the added species will increase, and this will tend to lower the concentration of the added species as well as the concentration of all other species it can react with. The increased rates of these reactions will tend to increase the concentrations of the products of the reactions. But as the concentrations of these products rise, they, in turn, will tend to react more rapidly. Eventually a new equilibrium state should be reached. All the reactions will be proceeding somewhat faster in the new state than in the original one, but for each reaction, forward and reverse rates would be equal, and the dynamic equilibrium state will have been restored. Removing a species has the reverse effect; all the reactions slow down until a new equilibrium state is reached.

The quantitative effect of adding or removing ingredients can be calculated from a knowledge of the stoichiometry, or molar relationships, of the reaction with the help of the equilibrium-constant expression. (Thus the net equation indicates the relative number of moles of each substance that will react. This stoichiometric information plus the equilibrium-constant expression usually allows a unique solution to the problem of what quantitative changes will occur.)

The Equilibrium State and Temperature Changes

The equilibrium state is determined by the fact that the rates of all opposing reactions must be identical at equilibrium. Now change in temperature also can affect the rates of reactions and, thus, may affect the equilibrium state.

Through applying the principle of microscopic reversibility we have seen that the equilibrium constant is actually the product of the rate constants for all the mechanistic steps involved in the equilibrium. (See equations 5.20 and 5.26.) Thus any effect on the rate constants should show up also in the equilibrium constant.

The effect of temperature on the rate constant is principally through the activation energy as shown in equation 3.10.

$$k = Ce^{-\Delta E^{\ddagger}/RT} \tag{5.29}$$

In a simple mechanistic step such as the hydrogen-iodine or glucose-hydroxide ion reactions, the equilibrium constant is given by the ratio of the constants for the forward and reverse reactions:

$$K_{eq} = \frac{k_{\text{reverse rate}}}{k_{\text{forward rate}}} = \frac{C_r e^{-\Delta E_r^{\ddagger}/RT}}{C_f e^{-\Delta E_f^{\ddagger}/RT}} = C' e^{-(\Delta E_r^{\ddagger} - \Delta E_f^{\ddagger})/RT} \tag{5.30}$$

We have shown that $\Delta E^{\ddagger}$ is the difference in energy between the reactants which give the complex and the activated complex. Thus, in general,

$$\Delta E^{\ddagger} = E_{\text{complex}} - E_{\text{reactants}} \tag{5.31}$$

Thus,

$$\triangle E^{\ddagger}_{\text{reverse}} = E_{\text{complex}} - E_{\text{products}} \qquad (5.32)$$

and

$$\triangle E^{\ddagger}_{\text{forward}} = E_{\text{complex}} - E_{\text{reactants}} \qquad (5.33)$$

Substituting 5.32 and 5.33 into 5.30 gives

$$K_{eq} = C'e^{-[(E_{\text{complex}} - E_{\text{reactants}}) - (E_{\text{complex}} - E_{\text{products}})]/RT} \qquad (5.34)$$

$$= C'e^{-[E_{\text{products}} - E_{\text{reactants}}]/RT} \qquad (5.35)$$

But

$$E_{\text{products}} - E_{\text{reactants}} = \triangle E, \text{ the net energy change in reaction.} \qquad (5.36)$$

Thus

$$K_{eq} = C'e^{-\triangle E/RT} \qquad (5.37)$$

An interesting inference from equation 5.37 is that the equilibrium constant, and hence the equilibrium state, should not be affected by the activation energy. Experimentally this is true. The sizes of the activation energies have no effect on the equilibrium state.

But also we note from equation 5.37 that the equilibrium constant does depend on the temperature, and also on the over-all energy of reaction. This theoretical prediction is again borne out by the experimental data. In fact, a plot of the logarithm of the equilibrium constant versus the reciprocal of the Kelvin temperature gives a straight line of slope, $-\triangle E/R$, as predicted by equation 5.37. Remember that a plot of the logarithm of the rate constant versus the reciprocal of the Kelvin temperature also gave a straight line. The slope there equaled $\triangle E^{\ddagger}/R$. (Those familiar with the full theoretical treatment will observe that we have maintained the use of $\triangle E$ throughout rather than introducing the concept of enthalpy and $\triangle H$. In almost all instances the numerical difference is very slight, and the simplification achieved by the treatment here should neither seriously mislead the reader, nor make it difficult for him to comprehend the more complete treatment later.)

The idea that the equilibrium state, that is, the extent of reaction, should depend on $\triangle E$ fits well with our discussion of bond strength. If $\triangle E$ is negative, energy is evolved by the reaction. This means that the bonds in the products are, on the average, stronger than those in the reactants. We presumed in Chapter 4 that strong bonds tend to form. And from equation

5.37 we see that large negative values of $\triangle E$ tend to give large values of K, indicating that such reactions do tend to occur to a considerable extent.

We thus arrive at the important result that the equilibrium state depends on the over-all energy change in the reaction, but that the rate depends on the activation energy. We may rationalize this in somewhat different terms by pointing out that the rate in the forward direction depends on the activation energy in that direction. The rate in the reverse direction depends on the activation energy in that direction. These two activation energies differ by exactly the energy of the reaction, and it is this difference in activation energies which helps determine the equilibrium constant and its variation with temperature.

Catalysts and the Equilibrium State

We find experimentally that catalysts never affect the equilibrium state or the equilibrium constant. A catalyst will decrease the time necessary to attain equilibrium, but it does not affect the concentrations present at equilibrium.

We can interpret this simply in terms of our previous discussion of the relationship between the equilibrium constant, the activation energies, and the over-all energy of reaction. The catalyst supplies a new mechanism for the reaction, but it does not change the over-all energy requirements since the initial and the final state are unaltered by the catalyst. The catalyst usually changes the rate by lowering the activation-energy requirement. But the change in activation energy has no effect on the equilibrium state and hence neither does a catalyst.

Since the catalyst has no effect on the equilibrium state but yet increases the rate of the forward reaction, and since at equilibrium the rates of the forward and reverse reactions must be identical, it follows that a catalyst must increase the rate of the reverse reaction by exactly the same factor as it increases the rate of the forward reaction. Experiment shows that this is so.

Orientation Effects and the Equilibrium State

The entropies of activation, that is, the orientation requirements, for the forward and reverse reactions will seldom be identical. The reaction with the less stringent orientation requirements—i.e., lower entropy of activation—will tend to be faster, and that with the more demanding requirements will tend to be slower. Thus the equilibrium will tend to favor high concentrations of those substances which have the greatest difficulty in meeting the orientational demands of the reaction. A catalyst may alter the activation entropies, but again the catalyst does not affect the equilibrium. It only affects the rates.

An enzyme system synthesizing proteins from simple amino acids might serve as an example. The protein requires a special, and often highly special, orientation of each amino acid before the addition can occur. Thus the rate of formation of protein may be small. Enzymes are biological catalysts, some of which catalyze protein synthesis. One of the effects of the enzyme may be to hold the amino acid in an orientation favorable to protein synthesis and thus to accelerate the synthetic reaction. The enzyme may thus lower the entropy of activation. But the enzyme also catalyzes the reverse reaction—the degradation of the protein—by exactly the same amount. No change in the final equilibrium occurs, but the rate of synthesis increases owing to the orientational assistance of the enzyme.

We shall discuss these entropy or configurational effects in more detail shortly since they can have as much influence on an equilibrium state as the concentration or energy and, in some cases, are the most important single effect.

The Tendency Toward Equilibrium

Reactants that have few configurational requirements and a low activation energy will react at almost every collision. Their concentration will rapidly decrease. Conversely, reactants with restrictive configurational requirements or high activation energies will seldom react, and their concentrations will tend to become large. In any given system, all possible reactions will occur, but those substances which react least often will tend to have the largest concentrations.

The net result of the random collisions predicted by the kinetic theory is to bring the system to a state of dynamic equilibrium. At dynamic equilibrium all possible reactions are occurring, and the rate of each forward reaction exactly equals the rate of its opposite, backward reaction. Low-energy collisions lead to simple rebounding, whereas high-energy collisions may lead to chemical reaction. The relative concentrations of the various species present at equilibrium depend on configurational and activation-energy requirements for their formation and reaction.

We might summarize these tendencies in somewhat different terms as follows: The fact that all atoms attract one another to a certain extent would tend to lead to the formation of a large number of chemical bonds around any given atom. On the other hand, once a given atom has formed a few bonds it becomes more and more unlikely that it can form further strong bonds. The most stable bonding arrangement in any system will, therefore, tend to be such that the bond strength is at a maximum rather than that the total number of bonds is at a maximum.

Thus each sodium atom in metallic sodium forms strong bonds to 8 other sodium atoms since this gives the maximum bond strength (stronger than arrangements involving 6 or 10 neighbors). On the other hand, most metals have 12 nearest neighbors in their crystalline state, indicating that for them this gives more strong bonds than any other arrangement.

Similarly, carbon can normally form four very strong bonds. But these four bonds do not preclude the existence of further bonds. As a result, methane, CH_4, placed in an atmosphere of hydrogen atoms might indeed form CH_5 molecules for a finite length of time. On the other hand, hydrogen atoms can bond so much more strongly to other hydrogen atoms than they can to methane molecules that the equilibrium situation would find present mainly methane molecules and hydrogen molecules rather than CH_5 molecules. But one must remember that, in the equilibrium state, there will still be a finite concentration of hydrogen atoms, that these will occasionally collide with methane molecules, and that there might be an occasional opportunity for a CH_5 molecule to exist for a very short period of time.

The existence of any hydrogen atoms at all, of course, is interpreted in terms of the occasional collisions of high-energy molecules. During such a collision, one hydrogen molecule may pick up so much energy that no stable vibrational state exists. It will then fly apart into hydrogen atoms. These two hydrogen atoms may then undergo many collisions before they find an opportunity to recombine and form another hydrogen molecule. (See page 56.) In the same way, methane molecules will occasionally be decomposed by collision into free hydrogen atoms and methyl radicals, CH_3, or even into methylene, CH_2, and two hydrogen atoms. At lower temperatures these latter species, in which the number of hydrogens connected to a carbon is small, get exceedingly rare. At high temperatures, on the other hand, the average collisions become so energetic that the existence of the larger molecules becomes more and more rare. Rotations, vibrations, and electronic states are so highly excited by the energetic collisions that decomposition becomes common, and simple monatomic and diatomic species predominate.

The final equilibrium state thus depends on the energy of possible bonds, the temperature of the system, and the available ways the atoms and energy may be distributed. In our studies of rates we identified these as energy, temperature, and entropy. It should not be surprising to find the same factors determining the equilibrium state.

Thus dynamic equilibrium involves competition among all the possible states for the limited number of atoms in the system. The random collisions lead to the formation of all possible molecules, but the equilibrium concentration of each kind of molecule will depend on the relative chances of its formation and reaction. These, in turn, depend on collision rates, temperature, energies, and orientational requirements.

Questions

1. Write rate equations for each of the following mechanistic steps:

    a. $F_2O_2 \rightarrow F_2 + O_2$
    b. $H + HBr \rightarrow H_2 + Br$
    c. $C_6H_5CHO + C_6H_5CHO + CN^- \rightarrow C_6H_5CH(OH)COC_6H_5 + CN^-$

2. Write equilibrium-constant expressions for each of the following net reactions. Compare these expressions to the rate equations you wrote for the same systems in problem 1.

    a. $F_2O_2 = F_2 + O_2$
    b. $H_2 + Br_2 = 2 HBr$
    c. $2 C_6H_5CHO = C_6H_5CH(OH)COC_6H_5$

3. Given the net reaction

$$CH_3COCH_3 + I_2 - CH_3COCH_2I + H^+ + I^-$$

would you expect an increase in the concentration of I_2 to have any effect on the rate of the reaction? On the concentrations present at equilibrium? Would you expect a change in the concentration of hydrogen ion to affect the rate? the equilibrium concentrations?

4. The actual rate equation for the reaction in problem 3 is

$$d(CH_3COCH_3)/dt = k(CH_3COCH_3)(H^+)$$

Suggest a possible mechanism.

5. Some $\triangle E^{\ddagger}$'s for the forward and reverse reactions are shown below in kcal/mole. Calculate the over-all energy of reaction, $\triangle E$, and predict the effect of a rise in temperature on each rate and on the concentrations present in each equilibrium state.

Reaction	$H_2 + I_2 \rightleftharpoons 2 HI$	$H + HBr \rightleftharpoons H_2 + Br$	$D + DBr \rightleftharpoons D_2 + Br$
$\triangle E^{\ddagger}_{forward}$	40	1.09	2.15
$\triangle E^{\ddagger}_{reverse}$	44	17.74	19.87

6

Energy

and Randomness

The kinetic theory initiated by Maxwell and Boltzmann depicts molecular behavior in terms similar to those we might use to describe wild animals running amok. According to the theory, molecules gyrate through space in a wildly random fashion—rotating, vibrating, and colliding. During a collision they may take one or two "bites" at each other. These bites will produce a change only if the orientation is suitable and if the bonds are weak enough to break because of the energy of the collision. And as in the animal kingdom, so with molecules, those survive and increase in number which have the least chance of undergoing collisions leading to destructive changes. Most collisions, of course, lead to change in the energies of the particles. The molecules gyrate more (or less) wildly after the collision depending on whether they gain (or lose) energy. But chemical reaction occurs only when new aggregates form as the result of a collision.

Given enough time, a dynamic equilibrium is reached in which the concentration of each aggregate is determined by the likelihood of its undergoing a collision that will lead to reaction. At dynamic equilibrium the rates of the forward and reverse reactions of each step become identical and no further net change occurs in the system.

Escaping Tendency

We may interpret the tendency to equilibrium in a slightly different fashion by introducing the term, "escaping tendency." Because of random kinetic energy, which depends on temperature, every atom will have a finite opportunity or tendency to escape from its present state into another state. If the atom is bound to a second atom, a high-energy collision may free it. If the atom is free, a low-energy collision may allow it to combine with another atom. A second low-energy collision may let the molecule grow larger. The random nature of the collisions and the great variety of their energies will assure that occasionally all possible combinations are realized, and each atom will spend part of its time in the free state, and part bonded to other atoms in various combinations.

How much time an atom spends in any given combination will depend greatly on the strength of the chemical bonds holding it in that combination, on the number of possible combinations, and on the available kinetic energy (temperature). The stronger the bonds, the longer the time it will be in that particular combination. Therefore, it is most likely that molecules containing strong bonds will be found in any equilibrium system. On the other hand, the higher the kinetic energy—i.e., the higher the temperature—the more likely it is that even strong bonds will be broken. At very high temperatures, it is extremely likely that a large number of free atoms will be present, and that only simple molecules such as diatomic ones with very strong bonds will be common. Collisions are so frequent and so energetic that more complex molecules, or molecules with weaker bonds, cannot exist for any appreciable length of time.

At very low temperatures, however, not only will the strong bonds be able to form, but so will many weak ones. As a result, methane, for example, will not only exist as CH_4 molecules, but the molecules themselves will cluster together to form liquid methane. At this temperature, the weak bonds between the molecules are strong enough to hold the molecules close to one another. At very low temperatures, even helium atoms, which exhibit the weakest interatomic forces known, will cluster together to form liquid helium. And at these temperatures escaping tendencies are low, and high concentrations of complex aggregations of atoms exist.

The escaping tendency is strongly affected by the temperature. It increases with increase in temperature because of the rapid rise in average kinetic energy of the molecules. Escaping tendency also increases with concentration. For example, increasing the concentration of a particular species in a gas increases the likelihood of its colliding with another reactive substance and of undergoing reaction. Conversely, the formation of strong bonds decreases the escaping tendency of a substance. For example, at low pressures and temperatures diamond slowly converts to graphite since the bond strength in graphite is, on the average, stronger than that in diamond.

Net reactions will occur until the relative concentrations of each kind of atom in all the molecular species present at equilibrium are such that the escaping tendency of an atom of any particular element is the same everywhere in the system. This equilibrium escaping tendency will have a minimum value since substances will always move from regions of higher to regions of lower escaping tendency. We shall now develop some ideas that will allow us to treat escaping tendency quantitatively.

Chemical Systems

We have now answered the question "Why do chemical reactions occur?" in terms of the kinetic theory, random collision processes, varying bond strengths, and various possible states. We have used qualitative description almost entirely. We certainly have not discussed how the decomposition of wood and the synthesis of wood can both occur, or how the rusting of iron and the reclamation of iron from iron oxide also both occur. Clearly we must do more than talk in generalities concerning the tendency to equilibrium if we are to discuss intelligently such actions which clearly are going in opposite directions and toward obviously different final states. In order to be more quantitative and to treat such systems with some success, we shall use the language of thermodynamics.

A careful comparison of the conditions on the inside and outside of the blast furnace, or in the rotting and growing trees, will show that the concentrations are comparable. Within the blast furnace the temperature is higher, and we can see that might be important. But in the case of the rotting and growing trees the temperatures are comparable. It is certainly true that the bond strengths are the same, since the same molecules are involved. How then can the escaping tendencies be so different, that in one case the wood is reacting with oxygen to produce carbon dioxide and water, and in the other case the carbon dioxide and water are reacting to produce oxygen and wood?

A close study of the two trees will reveal that at least one difference has to do with the energies involved in the reactions. Calorimetric measurements will show that the rotting wood is slowly evolving energy to the outside world, while the growing tree is absorbing energy from the surrounding sunlight. If we apply this observation to the iron system, we notice the same thing. The rusting iron is evolving energy to the rest of the world, and the blast-furnace reaction is absorbing energy as it converts iron oxide to iron. Of course, the high temperature inside the furnace aids the reaction that is absorbing energy. The conservation laws lead us to believe that the total energy of the universe is constant, but it is clear that the energy contents of those portions of the universe we are here interested in are changing. Before we concentrate on the energy effects, let us first develop the concept of a chemical system, a system being any part of the universe we are interested in. It is convenient to define three types of systems:

Isolated systems. These are completely uninfluenced by any external effects. In particular they cannot exchange energy or matter with any other systems. The universe is normally treated as an isolated system.

Closed systems. These cannot exchange matter with other systems, but can gain and lose energy. A sealed tube alternately placed in hot and cold surroundings would be an example of a closed system. It would gain and lose energy, but the mass of its contents would remain unchanged.

Open systems. These can exchange both matter and energy with other systems. A beaker of boiling water would be an example. The beaker can gain energy from the flame, lose it by evaporation, and lose mass by evaporation. The rusting iron, the blast furnace, and the rotting and growing trees would be considered open systems.

We normally describe these systems and their changes in terms of a set of variables, preferably those which are readily measured and easily manipulated. The most common variables used to describe chemical systems are pressure, volume, temperature, mass, and energy.

An open system, then, is one in which mass and energy may be varied. A closed system is one in which mass is fixed, but in which energy may vary. An isolated system is one in which neither mass nor energy can vary. It is often possible to vary pressure, volume, and temperature in any of these kinds of systems.

Some Basic Thermodynamics

Most chemists have acquired at least an intuitive understanding of the five variables—pressure, volume, temperature, mass, and energy. Few chemists feel uncomfortable describing a system in terms of such variables. There are, moreover, many useful variables and relationships which may be derived from these quantities, or stated in terms of them.

The very earliest developments in thermodynamics led to two general conclusions related to these variables. The first is the idea of *temperature equilibrium*. To be exact, if substance 1 is in thermal equilibrium with substance 2, and substance 2 is in thermal equilibrium with substance 3, then substance 1 is also in thermal equilibrium with substance 3. To put it another way, if substance 1 has the same temperature as substance 2, and if substance 2 has the same temperature as substance 3, then substance 1 has the same temperature as substance 3. The second is the idea of *the conservation of energy*. It can be stated that the total energy content of any isolated system is constant. Most chemists readily accept and use these two ideas.

A third major generalization was discovered almost 150 years ago. It is most unfortunate that this generalization is not widely understood and is unused by many chemists. A simple and reasonably exact statement of this principle is that *all processes* in isolated systems of constant volume tend to increase the disorder in the system. We have already cited one example of this, due to Maxwell, when we pointed out that, even should a set of molecules in the gas phase instantaneously have the same individual energies, they would very quickly redistribute these energies to follow the Maxwell-Boltzmann curve shown in Figure 3.4. The system would move from the ordered arrangement where every molecule had the same energy, to the more disordered arrangement in which the energies of the molecules differed.

The principle was also invoked implicitly when we interpreted chemical reactions as resulting from the random collision of molecules, and the tendency to a dynamic equilibrium in which all possible configurations were represented rather than only the most strongly bonded one.

Entropy

This randomness factor can be measured quantitatively and is given the name *entropy*. We met entropy before in terms of orientational effects

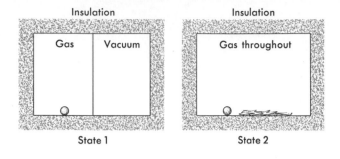

FIGURE 6.1 *The entropy increases when a gas spontaneously diffuses into a vacuum in an isolated system. The energy, mass, and total volume of the system remain constant.*

on rates of reactions. The entropy change in a given closed or isolated system can be simply defined as $\triangle S = R \log \dfrac{(\text{disorder in state})_2}{(\text{disorder in state})_1}$. (Notice that this parallels completely our earlier representation of $\triangle S^{\ddagger}$.) It is not possible for us here to develop the theory of disorder completely, nor have we space to apply the entropy concept to many chemical systems. But we can develop a few examples to show its power.

Let us first consider the isolated system of gas shown in Figure 6.1. No energy or mass can leave the insulated system, which consists of two equal volumes separated by a glass partition. The left-hand volume contains a fixed quantity of gas and a metal ball. The right-hand volume is completely evacuated. If the barrier is now shattered by the ball, the gas proceeds to fill the whole container. The system is isolated, hence the change cannot be interpreted in terms of gain or loss in energy. But, it can be interpreted in terms of a change of entropy. In state 1, it was certain that every gas molecule would be in the left-hand side of the container. Disorder does exist, however, in the gas. In state 2, the disorder is twice as great since the available volume for gaseous motion is twice as great. Thus, change in entropy is equal to R logarithm 2 over 1, or $\triangle S = R \log 2$. The system has moved from a more ordered to a more disordered arrangement. The entropy has increased.

Or consider a drop of liquid in a glass bulb mounted in an evacuated, insulated chamber as shown in Figure 6.2. If the glass bulb is broken the liquid immediately begins to evaporate until the vaporized molecules exert a pressure equal to the equilibrium vapor pressure of the liquid. Again the total energy of the system is constant, but the drop of water cools off since some of its kinetic energy must go into evaporating the liquid. Thus, the drop of water spontaneously loses kinetic energy. But again notice that the entropy of the system has increased. The disorder in the closely packed molecular arrangements found in a drop of water is considerably less than that found in the gas. The volume available per molecule is much greater in the gas than in the liquid. Gas disorder, as represented by freedom of motion, is much greater than liquid disorder. The complete calculation of the entropy change is not as simple here as in the example above because

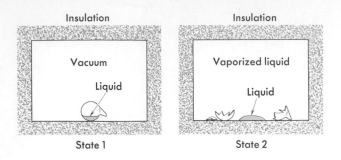

FIGURE 6.2 *The entropy increases when a liquid vaporizes in an isolated system. The energy, mass, and volume of the system remain constant.*

not enough is known about the disorder of the various states which the molecules might have in the droplet of liquid.

But we can do a rough calculation of $\triangle S$. Just as with the previous example there is a large increase in the volume available to the water molecules. The volume of gaseous water at room temperature is approximately 50,000 times that of the same weight of liquid. Due to this change in volume the disorder has increased 50,000 times. $\triangle S = R \log 50,000 = 22$ cal/mole °K. We know from independent measurements that the actual $\triangle S$ for this change is about 30 cal/mole °K, quite a bit larger than we have calculated. But the gaseous molecules have a great deal of freedom, especially rotational, that the liquid did not, and the increased "disorder" from the increased random motions in the gas must be included in the experimental figure.

For a third example consider Figure 6.3. Here again we have an insulated system which may be manipulated to drop the solid into the liquid. Some of the solid spontaneously dissolves. Again the entropy of the system increases. It is easy to see that the entropy will increase, since the arrangement in the regular crystal packing is much more ordered than the arrangement of dissolved particles in the solution.

From these and many other examples, it has become possible to find a perfectly general criterion for change in any isolated system: it is, that the entropy of the system will increase. This is to say that such a system is always more disordered after it has changed than it was before the change. We can even say that change occurs because of the natural tendency to increase disorder. But note, the universal increase in entropy is only characteristic of an isolated system of constant volume.

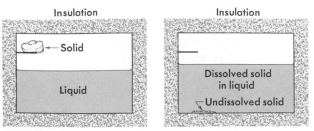

FIGURE 6.3 *The entropy increases when a solid dissolves in liquid in an isolated system. The energy, mass, and volume of the system remain constant.*

It should be clear that this may allow us to predict which changes will occur if we can decide ahead of time which is the more ordered and which the more disordered state. In a constant-volume isolated system, only changes which take the system toward a more disordered state will occur.

We see that the tendency for entropy (or disorder) to increase fits well with our previous discussion of escaping tendency. All atoms, because of their random motions, tend to leave or escape from where they are. They tend to mix, spread out, diffuse. One of the important measures of this tendency to escape is the entropy—a quantitative measure of the tendency for disorder to increase.

Since the universe is normally considered an isolated system of constant volume, we have a simple criterion for all total changes which we observe in the universe. All such changes result in an increase of disorder in the universe as a whole. We must remember, however, that it is possible to treat small portions of the universe as closed systems or as open systems. The entropy change in a closed system or an open system may be either positive, negative, or zero, but the entropy change in an isolated system is always positive. The isolated system always goes from a more ordered to a less ordered arrangement in any change.

Quantitative Criteria for Change

A few quantitative criteria for change are listed in Table 6.1. The first column gives the type of system. The second column lists the conditions held constant during the change under consideration. The third column gives the quantitative criteria for the direction of the change.

Table 6.1   QUANTITATIVE CRITERIA FOR CHANGE
IN A FEW TYPES OF SYSTEMS *

System	Constant	Criterion for Direction of Change
Isolated	Energy and volume	Disorder (entropy) goes to a maximum. $\triangle S$ is positive.
Closed	Pressure and temperature	Free energy goes to a minimum. $\triangle G$ is negative.
Open	No simple general criteria available. In general, does not reach equilibrium. Change occurs so long as loss or gain of mass and/or energy from the system is maintained.	

* Many other types of systems are possible.

Chemists operate with systems fitting into all the categories shown, plus other categories which are not described in the table. Very common conditions in the laboratory are those of constant pressure and constant temperature. For these conditions, you will see that the table lists the criterion that the free energy of the system will always tend toward a minimum. For our purposes, the change in free energy in a closed system at constant temperature and pressure may be defined by the equation $\triangle G = \triangle H - T\triangle S$. $\triangle H$, called the change in heat content or enthalpy, is the quantity of heat that would be gained by the closed system if the change were carried out in a calorimeter at constant pressure and constant temperature. T is the Kelvin temperature, and $\triangle S$ is the change in entropy, or order, as defined earlier. $\triangle G$, the change in free energy, is the difference between the heat and entropy (times temperature) term. All these terms can be measured quantitatively in the laboratory. It is possible to show that change in free energy can also be described as the maximum possible work in excess of that due to any volume change.

We have now developed several ideas concerning thermodynamics. Let us clarify them by discussing some particular examples.

Changes in Isolated Systems at Constant Volume

According to Table 6.1 changes in isolated systems at constant volume always occur in such a direction as to increase the disorder in the system. Since both the energy and the mass content of an isolated system are constant, increased disorder must result from energy or mass flow. We can have energy flow from one place to another, and/or mass movement from one place to another, within the system.

Thus, in an isolated system, net heat can only flow spontaneously from a hotter to a colder region, never the reverse. The energies of the hotter and colder systems become mixed and will not spontaneously unmix. Less order (for instance, in terms of the separation of hot and cold molecules) exists than before.

Order is also associated with aggregates of atoms. Pure substances are more ordered than solutions. Crystals are more ordered than liquids, and liquids more than gases. Polyatomic molecules are more ordered than simpler molecules from which they may be formed. Furthermore, spontaneous processes in nature always tend toward the decomposition of ordered structures into structures of less order. Buildings tend to fall apart, solids tend to dissolve in liquids, or to evaporate as gases, or to decompose in other ways, by rotting, for example.

In most actual processes, changes occur as a result of a combination of energy flow and shifts in the order of chemical species. Thus rotting normally is exothermic and also leads to the formation of simple molecules. Both the transfer of energy to other parts of the system and the formation of simpler molecules are spontaneous processes and the rotting will proceed to completion as long as the energy can leave the rotting log and, together with the other products of the rotting process, enter the rest of the system.

On the other hand, a tree may absorb the high energy of sunlight in a spontaneous fashion and with a large increase in order. There is still a net loss of order since the source of the light has lost more order than the leaf has gained. Some of this absorbed energy can then be used to create molecular order within the leaf, and, for example, through the reaction of carbon dioxide and water, produce complicated plant material and oxygen. The absorption of light and the accompanying molecular change involve an increase in order, but the emission of light from the sun involves an even larger decrease in order. So long as the decrease in order resulting from the loss in the sun is greater than the increase in order resulting from the molecular change in the leaf, the over-all result is a decrease in order and the process is spontaneous. The over-all reaction continues to occur in the direction of net increase of disorder.

We see then that chemical reactions in isolated systems will occur if the over-all effect of all energy and molecular changes is to create net disorder. We may generalize as follows:

1) Any reaction which is both exothermic and creates simpler molecules is probable, since each of these processes increases the disorder in the universe.

2) Any reaction which is both endothermic and creates more ordered molecules is improbable, since each of these processes decreases the disorder in the universe.

The other combinations—3) exothermic reactions which create more ordered molecules, and 4) endothermic reactions which create simpler molecules—will be probable if there is a net decrease in order as a result of counterbalancing of the energy and molecular-order effects.

We must talk about the probability of reaction because the random nature of molecular collisions and the Maxwell-Boltzmann distribution of molecular energies make all reactions possible. A probable reaction is one that occurs to a considerable extent. The rate may be slow, but at equilibrium large amounts of reactants have been converted to products. Here are examples of each of the four types of reactions given above:

1. Exothermic reactions giving simpler molecules will always occur: e.g., combustion of most fuels made of complicated molecules such as wood, coal, petroleum.

2. Endothermic reactions giving more ordered molecules will occur only when a high-energy source is available in which the loss of order is greater than the gain in order in the endothermic part of the system—e.g., photosynthesis.

3. Exothermic reactions which create more ordered aggregates occur only when energy loss to other parts of system creates enough disorder there to balance gain in order within the exothermic portion of the system: e.g., most precipitation reactions, condensation of gases to liquids, and liquids to solids.

4. Endothermic reactions which create disorder in the same part of the system occur only when increase in molecular disorder in this part of the system is large enough to counterbalance energy change: e.g., evaporation of a liquid or solid, most reactions involving formation of a solution, most thermal decompositions.

Examination of the above will show that exothermic reactions are probable unless there is a large counterbalancing effect of gain in molecular order. On the other hand, endothermic reactions are improbable unless there is a large counterbalancing effect due to loss in order. Most observed chemical reactions, are, therefore, exothermic.

Yet it should be equally clear that it is impossible to predict the probability of a reaction from energetics alone.* Molecular order must also be considered. Changes in an isolated system are never reversible. Such reversal would mean a decrease in entropy of the system and this has never been observed in an isolated system.

Changes in Closed Systems at Constant Temperature and Pressure

As mentioned earlier, many systems of interest in the laboratory are closed systems of constant mass and varying energy. Changes in closed systems are easier to visualize than those in isolated systems, since usually we do not concern ourselves with the energy flowing within the system,

* It should also be remembered that probabilities in terms of equilibrium and reaction velocity are not synonymous. See page 6.

but only with its net flow into and out of the system. At constant pressure, the energy change in a closed system is known as $\triangle H$, positive if energy is gained by the system.

The general relation in a closed system at constant T and P (as mentioned on page 88) is $\triangle G = \triangle H - T\triangle S$, where processes with a negative value of $\triangle G$ are probable and those with a positive value of $\triangle G$ are improbable. (See Table 6.1.)

Considering only the $\triangle H$ factor, we see that exothermic reactions (negative $\triangle H$) are probable and endothermic reactions (positive $\triangle H$) are improbable because of their effect on the sign of $\triangle G$. Furthermore, as T approaches $0°K$ (and, therefore, $T\triangle S$ approaches zero) only the $\triangle H$ is important in determining the sign and magnitude of $\triangle G$. Thus, at very low temperatures, the probability of reaction is determined solely by the sign and magnitude of $\triangle H$.

Since T is always positive, the sign of $\triangle S$ determines the effect of the $T\triangle S$ term on $\triangle G$. If $\triangle S$ is positive, $(-T\triangle S)$ becomes more and more negative as T increases, and the reaction becomes more and more probable as the temperature rises (assuming $\triangle H$ does not change with changing T). Actually $\triangle H$ usually changes with T, but the change is usually fairly slow. Similarly, if $\triangle S$ is negative, the likelihood of reaction decreases with rise in T, since $(-T\triangle S)$ becomes more and more positive. At very large values of T, the sign of the $T\triangle S$ term uniquely determines the likelihood of reaction, since the $\triangle H$ term becomes negligible compared to the ever increasing $T\triangle S$ term.

For most reactions near room temperature, $T\triangle S$ is small compared to $\triangle H$. Thus, under normal laboratory conditions of constant temperature and pressure in a closed system, exothermic reactions are generally probable ($\triangle G$ is usually negative), and endothermic reactions are generally improbable ($\triangle G$ is usually positive).

At high temperatures the sign of $\triangle S$ determines the sign of $\triangle G$ since $T\triangle S$ becomes large. $\triangle S$ will, in general, be positive if large aggregates are decomposing into small aggregates. Thus, for $H_2O \rightarrow H_2 + \frac{1}{2}O_2$, $\triangle S$ will be positive. At high temperatures this reaction will occur to a greater degree than at low temperatures.

Note that we can extrapolate the last paragraph to indicate that at very high temperatures all complex molecules will become rare and there will be no probable chemical reactions among the atomic fragments to form larger molecules. Thus almost no atomic aggregates will be found at temperatures above $100,000°K$. At this temperature, and even more at higher temperatures, even the atoms disintegrate into electrons and ions because of the high collision energies. Above $10^{6}°K$, nuclei and electrons are the principal species present in a gas. At still higher temperatures nuclei disintegrate into protons and neutrons.

Numerical values for G may, for example, be calculated from a knowledge of $\triangle H$, $\triangle S$, and their variation with temperature. The sign of $\triangle H$ may be predicted from a knowledge of bond strengths. If the bond strengths of the product molecules are stronger than those of the reactant molecules, $\triangle H$ will be negative. Thus, in the reaction $NH_4NO_2 \longrightarrow N_2 + 2\,H_2O$, both N_2 and H_2O are known to have strong bonds. Thus $\triangle H$ is probably negative and the reaction shown will be probable at low temperatures (although it may be very slow if the activation energy is high).

Similarly, the sign of $\triangle S$ may often be guessed by counting the moles of reactants and products. Since $\triangle S$ is positive for an increase in disorder, that reaction producing the most molecules (especially gaseous molecules) will probably have a positive sign for $\triangle S$. In the reaction $NH_4NO_{2(s)} = N_{2(g)} + 2\,H_2O_{(g)}$ we would guess $\triangle S$ to be positive since three moles of gas form from one mole of solid. Thus $T\triangle S$ is positive and the reaction becomes more and more probable as the temperature rises, since $\triangle G = \triangle H - T\triangle S$, and a negative $\triangle G$ indicates a probable reaction.

For the reaction $H_2 + \frac{1}{2}\,O_2 = H_2O$, $\triangle H$ is negative (the bonds in H_2O are strong), but $\triangle S$ is probably also negative. (The number of molecules decreases.) Therefore this reaction will be probable at lower temperatures, but will become less and less probable as the temperature is raised. (But remember that the rate of reaction may be small at low temperatures.)

For the reaction $CO + N_2O = CO_2 + N_2$, we would guess a negative $\triangle H$ since CO_2 and N_2 bonds are so strong. $\triangle S$ should be approximately zero (since there is no change in molecular complexities). Thus the reaction should have a $-\triangle G$ value at all temperatures and should be a probable reaction. We must, of course, remember that the reaction will occur with an appreciable rate only if the activation energy is not too high compared to the average kinetic energy of the molecules.

The sign of $\triangle G$ indicates the direction toward equilibrium, whereas the magnitude of $\triangle G$ indicates the distance from equilibrium. Thus if $\triangle G = 0$ the reaction is at equilibrium, whereas if $\triangle G$ has a large negative value a good deal of reaction will occur before equilibrium is reached. However, the rate of reaction has no correlation either with the sign or magnitude of $\triangle G$ and cannot be predicted from a knowledge of $\triangle G$.

For the reaction $CaCO_{3(s)} \longrightarrow CaO_{(s)} + CO_{2(g)}$, we would predict a positive value of $\triangle H$ since $CaCO_3$ is tightly bonded, and a positive value for $\triangle S$ since a mole of gas and a mole of solid are produced from one mole of solid. Thus the equilibrium will favor $CaCO_{3(s)}$ at low temperatures and gaseous CO_2 and solid CaO at higher temperatures.

Similar arguments would hold for reactions such as:

$$NH_4Cl_{(s)} \rightarrow NH_{3(g)} + HCl_{(g)}$$
$$ZnCl_{2(s)} + H_2O_{(g)} \rightarrow 2\,HCl_{(g)} + ZnO_{(s)}$$

Notice the ready comparison between $\triangle G$ and escaping tendency. The tendency of a particle to escape may be described in terms of its random motions (related to entropy changes, $\triangle S$, and temperature, T) and its bond strengths (related to enthalpy changes, $\triangle H$). Atoms tend to escape readily from states where they are loosely bonded ($\triangle H$ negative), and from states where they are concentrated and highly ordered ($\triangle S$ positive). The escaping tendency toward greater disorder always increases with rise in temperature. All this fits the quantitative formulation $\triangle G = \triangle H - T\triangle S$.

Changes in Open Systems

An open system differs from an isolated or a closed system in that substances can enter or leave. It is impossible in a closed system to have any reaction proceed to completion since the random collisions between the products will occasionally regenerate the reagents. Reactions may be even less complete in a small isolated system since, in addition, energy is conserved and exothermic reactions cannot "get rid of" the energy they produce and go further to completion.

In an open system, however, it is possible in principle to have reactions go to completion. Not only can energy escape to the surroundings (as in a closed system) making a reversal of the reaction through high-energy collision more unlikely, the products themselves may be dispersed or separated so that they cannot collide and reform the reactants.

Consider again the reaction $CaCO_{3(s)} \longrightarrow CaO_{(s)} + CO_2$. In a closed system the reaction will proceed to an equilibrium condition where $CaCO_3$ is decomposing at the same rate CaO and CO_2 are reacting upon collision to form $CaCO_3$. If the CO_2 is swept out of the furnace, as by a current of air, its reaction with the CaO becomes impossible and all the $CaCO_3$ will decompose.

It is for this reason that many chemical reactions are carried out under open-system conditions, especially if the equilibrium conditions are not favorable to the desired reaction. Thus coal is burned in an open fire box, cement is formed in an open heater, sea water is evaporated in an open pond to obtain salt, blast furnaces operate with a steady throughput of fresh air, petroleum is converted to gasoline in a continuous flow process, and ammonia synthesis is accompanied by continual removal of the ammonia in a cyclic process.

Under conditions of an open system, chemical reactions may be irreversible, that is, they can "go to completion," but solely because some of the products are removed and are no longer present to react. In isolated systems, chemical reactions are irreversible because energy will not spontaneously flow from a cold to a hot place, and because atoms will not spontaneously unmix. Irreversibility is not due to inability to react. Reactions occur continually and the system comes to a dynamic equilibrium. They do not "go to completion."

In a closed system, chemical reactions may be reversed simply by reversing the energy flows and they are reversible in any case except at absolute zero. Even in open systems reactions may be reversed by reversing the system. Thus $CaCO_3$ decomposes completely into CO_2 and CaO if heated in such a way that the CO_2 escapes. In principle, the reaction can be completely reversed if the system is cooled and the pressure of carbon dioxide is maintained above the equilibrium value.

The fact that the complete reversal of some reactions is not feasible in closed or open systems depends either on a slow rate or the difficulty of separating one of the reactants or products from the rest of the system rather than on a fundamental property of "reversibility" or "irreversibility."

We now see that the blast furnace which converts iron oxide to iron, and its outer surface which converts iron to iron oxide are examples of open systems. On the inside, coke is introduced and oxides of carbon removed so that virtually all the iron oxide is converted to iron. On the outside, iron reacts with oxygen to form the oxide. The pressure of oxygen in the atmosphere is far above that which would exist at the equilibrium between iron and iron oxide. Essentially all the metal would eventually be converted to oxide. Only rarely would an energetic region of the oxide crystal eject some oxygen and revert to iron.

Both the growing and the rotting trees also are best considered open systems. The growing tree ingests carbon dioxide, water, and energy (among other things) and gives up oxygen while producing tissue. The rotting tree reacts with oxygen and liberates energy, carbon dioxide, and water (among other things). The main difference is that energy is gained by the growing tree and lost by the rotting one, but the difference in processes is also partially due to the means each system has of accumulating or eliminating substances such as carbon dioxide, water, and oxygen. For example, the rotting proceeds until no wood is left, that is, to completion, since the products of reaction (including energy) escape and their concentration never rises to the level where equilibrium could be attained.

Questions

1. Predict the sign of the ΔH and $T\Delta S$ terms for each of the following reactions. Which species would be favored at equilibrium in each case at low temperatures? At high temperatures? Why does each reaction occur as it does at each temperature? Assume a closed system, constant T and P.

   a. $C_2H_5OH_{(g)} = C_2H_{4(g)} + H_2O_{(g)}$
   b. $CO_{(g)} + Cl_{2(g)} = COCl_{2(g)}$
   c. $C_3H_{8(g)} + 5\,O_{2(g)} = 3\,CO_{2(g)} + 4\,H_2O_{(g)}$
   d. $NH_4NO_{3(s)} = N_2O_{(g)} + 2\,H_2O_{(g)}$
   e. $AgCl_{(s)} = Ag^+{}_{(aq)} + Cl^-{}_{(aq)}$
   f. $2\,CO_{(g)} = CO_{2(g)} + C_{(s)}$
   g. $C_{(s)} + H_2O_{(g)} = CO_{(g)} + H_{2(g)}$

2. Values for the molar enthalpy of formation and for the entropy of each compound may be determined experimentally. The changes in enthalpy (ΔH) during reactions may then be calculated by taking the differences between the sums of the enthalpies of formation of the products and subtracting the sums of the enthalpies of formation of the reactants. ΔS for the reaction can be calculated similarly. Then ΔG can be calculated. Its sign tells which reaction is probable and its magnitude indicates the extent of reaction which must occur before equilibrium will be reached. Use the accompanying table and predict the net reaction which would occur at constant T and P if equal numbers of moles of all the chemicals listed were mixed in each case. That is, would each net reaction proceed in the forward or reverse direction as the system approached equilibrium? Estimate which reaction would be closest to equilibrium immediately after the chemicals were mixed and which would be farthest from equilibrium at these conditions. Predict the relative tendencies to occur of the forward and reverse reactions if each set of chemicals were mixed at a higher temperature.

   The table (p.96) shows some enthalpies of formation and entropies of gases at 298°K. ΔH = cal/mole; S = cal/mole °K. All elements are arbitrarily assigned zero values for $\Delta H_{formation,298°K}$. The entropies of all pure substances are based on values of $S = 0$ for each substance at 0°K.

Substance	$\Delta H_{formation, 298°K}$	$S_{298°K}$	Substance	$\Delta H_{formation, 298°K}$	$S_{298°K}$
H_2	0	31.211	H_2O	$-57,797.9$	45.106
O_2	0	49.01	CO	$-26,415.7$	47.20
Cl_2	0	53.29	CO_2	$-94,051.8$	51.08
SO_2	$-70,960$	59.40	C_2H_4	12,600	52.45
SO_3	$-94,450$	61.2	C_2H_6	$-20,200$	54.85
			HCl	$-22,063$	44.64

All reactants are gaseous. Assume a closed system, constant T and P.

a. $SO_2 + \frac{1}{2} O_2 = SO_3$

b. $CO + H_2O = CO_2 + H_2$

c. $2 H_2 + O_2 = 2 H_2O$

d. $H_2 + SO_3 = H_2O + SO_2$

e. $H_2 + C_2H_4 = C_2H_6$

f. $2 HCl = H_2 + Cl_2$

SUGGESTED FURTHER READING

Three references are listed under each general topic: (1) a discussion of experiments; (2) a brief, relatively elementary treatment; and (3) a comprehensive, moderately high-level treatment. Each reference listed contains many additional references for those interested in a more comprehensive approach. A good general reference at the college undergraduate level is W. J. Moore, *Physical Chemistry* (Englewood Cliffs, N. J.: Prentice-Hall, 1962).

MECHANISMS OF REACTIONS

1. Moews, P. C., Jr., and R. H. Petrucci, "The Oxidation of Iodide Ion by Persulfate Ion," *J. Chem. Educ.*, 41 (1964), 549–51.
2. King, E. L., *How Chemical Reactions Occur*. New York: Benjamin, 1963.
3. Benson, S., *The Foundations of Chemical Kinetics*. New York: McGraw-Hill, 1960.

MOLECULAR MOTIONS

1. Stafford, F. E., "Bond Spectra and Dissociation Energies," *J. Chem. Educ.*, 39 (1962), 626–29.
2. Barrow, G. M., *The Structure of Molecules*. New York: Benjamin, 1963.
3. Barrow, G. M., *Introduction to Molecular Spectroscopy*. New York: McGraw-Hill, 1962.

CHEMICAL ENERGETICS AND EQUILIBRIUM

1a. Bent, H. A., "The Second Law of Thermodynamics," *J. Chem. Educ.*, 39 (1962), 491–99.
1b. Symposium, "The Teaching of Thermodynamics," *J. Chem. Educ.*, 39 (1962), 490–510.
2. Mahan, B. H., *Elementary Chemical Thermodynamics*. New York: Benjamin, 1963.
3. Denbigh, K., *The Principles of Chemical Equilibrium*. Cambridge, England: Cambridge University Press, 1957.

Hints and Answers to Questions

Hints and Answers to Questions

1. *Hint.* Consider the amount of energy involved in the change. If the amount of energy is small, probably only weak bonds were broken or formed (although it is also possible that the amount of energy change is small due to bonds of equal strength being broken and formed). More insight is given by considering whether new substances form substances with properties very different from those of the original substances present. Finally it is necessary to consider whether the process might only have involved single atoms undergoing change with no change in their bonds to other atoms.

Answer. (a) Carbon and oxygen disappear; carbon dioxide and a great deal of energy are released. Carbon atoms were originally bonded to carbon atoms and oxygens to oxygen. In the products, carbon atoms and oxygen atoms are bonded together. The former's strong bonds break, and the latter's stronger bonds form. (b) Graphite is rubbed from the pencil lead onto the paper with very little effort. Initially the carbon atoms were bound only to other carbon atoms in the graphite. Finally, since the graphite sticks to the paper, the carbon atoms must be bound to those in the paper. These latter bonds are rather weak, as shown by the ease with which the pencil mark may be erased. (c) The interatomic forces holding solid sugar together are comparatively weak, as shown by the ease with which sugar may be ground or broken. Little energy change occurs when sugar dissolves in water, so the bonds between sugar and water must be equally weak. Note that the existence of weak bonds which break and form when the sugar dissolves does not mean that only weak bonds are present in sugar. Actually there are molecules (groups of atoms) present in the sugar both in the solid and the solution which are held together by very strong bonds. These bonds are virtually unaffected by the solution process. (d) Iron and oxygen plus some water disappear during rusting and the new substance, rust, forms. The bonds between iron and iron, between oxygen and oxygen, and between water and water have probably broken. New bonds between these three substances form as the rust appears. It is difficult to estimate the energy involved since it is liberated so slowly. We do know that a great deal of energy is required in the blast furnace to reverse the process. Hence strong bonds must be broken and/or formed in rusting. (e) Little energy is involved in stretching a rubber band and it readily returns to its original form, apparently unaltered. But it does change form in the process. Hence weak bonds holding it in the "relaxed" form are probably broken in the stretching process, or at least considerably deformed. The existence of considerably stronger bonds which are not affected by simple stretching is indicated by the great resistance to further stretch a rubber band exhibits when it is greatly stretched. When stretched beyond this "elastic limit," stronger bonds do break and the band does not return to its original condition when the stress is removed. (f) Emission of gamma rays leaves the iron ostensibly unaltered. All of its bulk properties are the same except for the total energy content, which has decreased. We attribute this process to a nuclear change which leaves the interatomic forces unchanged.

2. *Hint.* Almost any change can be analyzed in these terms.

Answer. Here are a few possibilities: (a) Applying the brakes to stop a car forms new bonds between the brake shoe and the drum. These last only momentarily, then dissociate transferring the energy of motion of the car into heat in the brake drum. If one "sets the brakes," stronger bonds form there, and bonds make and break between the tires and the street surface leading to squealing. Thus, these frictional processes involve making and breaking bonds. (b) Oiling a bicycle makes new and relatively strong bonds between the metal surfaces and the oil. The oil separates the metal surfaces from one another and decreases their chances to bond and "rub." Since the oil bonds only weakly to itself, friction is reduced. (c) Toasting bread not only makes it crisp, but also converts the starch into sugarlike products which taste sweeter. (d) Eating involves ingesting complicated substances (foods) and digesting them into simpler and simpler substances until carbon dioxide and water are finally formed as principal products. The process releases a large amount of energy which keeps the body warm and supports bodily processes and motion. (e) Boiling liquids involves breaking the bonds which hold the molecules together in the liquid and freeing the molecules to move comparatively independently of one another in the gas. Similarly, melting a solid loosens the bonds holding it together, and dissolving breaks the bonds holding it together. (f) Thinking (or using any of the senses) involves very complicated chemical changes in which electrical currents are generated by making and breaking bonds between atoms. The currents are carried through the body, again through changes in chemical bonds, and lead to a response somewhere in the body, again through the making and breaking of bonds between atoms.

3. *Hint.* Consider the conditions in nature under which fusion and fission become likely compared to conditions found in the chemical laboratory.

Answer. Fission and fusion of atoms do occur in every chemical laboratory, but only with very great rarity. Such reactions only become common at conditions of very high temperature and pressure such as found in the stars or in nuclear explosions, or under the very special conditions produced in nuclear power plants. In an ordinary laboratory the occurrence of fission or fusion reactions is so rare as to be well below the experimentally detectable limit in all ordinary chemical measurements.

4. *Hint.* Pick a rather simple change such as an object falling to the ground, lighting a fire, turning on a flashlight, etc. Physiological responses such as reading, moving, and using any of the senses get very complicated if you really attempt to analyze the mechanism.

Answer. Here is a possible mechanism for turning on a flashlight. (a) Pick up flashlight. (b) Depress the switch. (c) Chemical reactions begin in dry cells. (d) Electrons flow in completed circuit. (e) Filament becomes hot. (f) Light is emitted. Notice that we have not given a complete mechanism, because obviously the chemical reactions within the dry cells have their own mechanism. Furthermore, each of the other "simple" steps mentioned above could be analyzed into still simpler steps. Thus, we might discuss in detail how the electrons move through the circuit, or how the heating occurs in the filament, or how the light is emitted. The same thing is true of most kinetic mechanisms for chemical reactions. We discuss the motions of the molecules, but do not analyze the changes in terms of electronic behavior.

5. *Answer*. Complete reactions: combustion reactions involving solids; unstirred intermingling of two gases; unstirred mutual solution of many pairs of liquids (alcohol, glycerine, water); and corrosion of metals. All involve slow rate of contact between reactants. Quick attainment of equilibrium: explosions in gaseous mixtures (whether equilibrium is measurable depends on gases), evaporation of liquids in closed containers; and solution of solids in liquids accomplished with shaking. They often involve good mixing of reactants, high temperatures, or large energy changes.

One must be careful not to confuse "steady states" with equilibrium. Steady states involve no net change in the intermediate steps but always involve a net throughput of material. For example, the oceans and rivers are close to a steady state in that the volume of water in each remains virtually constant. But there is a directional flow at all times, maintained, in this case, by evaporation from the ocean and rainfall replenishment of the streams. Similarly many biological populations are sometimes said to be in "equilibrium" with their environments in the sense of no net change, but the actual states are steady states and not equilibria, since the absence of net change is maintained by a birth input and a death output, not by equal and opposite rates of two opposing, but otherwise identical, reactions.

CHAPTER 2

1. *Hint*. What substance burns and where does it come from?

Answer. A candle flame involves the reaction of hot gaseous wax with oxygen from the air. The wax must be vaporized and heated before it can collide with and react with the molecules of gaseous oxygen. Heating the wick with a match vaporizes and heats some of the wax on the wick. This small amount of wax is quickly consumed, however, and more cannot get to the flame until some of the solid wax of the candle melts and flows up the wick. This will only happen when the bottom of the flame gets close enough to the solid wax to melt it by radiation. This happens when the flame dies down. If the used wick is initially short, one will not observe a larger flame at the ignition since there is so little wax on the wick.

2. *Hint*. How does the foil alter the relationship of flame and candle?

Answer. Aluminum foil is a good reflector of heat as well as a good conductor. Normally a candle flame burns some distance above the solid wax and radiant energy from the bottom of the flame melts wax at just the right rate to maintain the flame in its steady-state condition. Inserting the foil decreases the radiated heat reaching the wax. Less wax melts and reaches the wick, so the flame diminishes in size and moves down the wick. As the bottom of the flame nears the foil the amount of conductive heating of the foil rises, melting wax on the other side of the foil. The melted wax flows up the wick and the flame grows large again. This cycle repeats many times. Usually the candle will eventually go out since the wick gets too short to maintain the large flame which must periodically form close to the foil in order to melt sufficient wax to get through the next cycle.

3. *Hint*. Do not be too detailed in breaking the mechanisms into tiny steps. Rather, group fast reactions into single "steps" and look for a likely slow, simple step.

Answer. (a) Find a piece of wood. Heat it to the kindling temperature. Assure that enough of the evolved heat is returned to the wood to maintain its surface at the kindling temperature. (The kindling temperature is that needed to volatilize enough combustible gases to maintain the flame.) Which is the rate-determining step depends on the conditions. Any of the steps listed could be the slowest, depending on the availability of wood, matches, etc. Notice that ordinarily it is very difficult to burn a single piece of wood since too little of the evolved heat is returned to the surface. Hence the saying, "It takes three logs to make a fire." (b) Active research is still in progress on this problem but here is a possibility. The temperature of the cloud must be neither too high nor too low. Nucleation of the tiny cloud droplets must occur into the larger drops which can fall as rain. Air between the cloud and ground must not be too dry. Drops must fall from cloud to ground. Again any of these could be the rate-determining step depending on the conditions. The step on which most "rain makers" concentrate is nucleation. Most successful induction of rain seems to have depended on successful nucleation, but the other conditions must, of course, have been reached. (c) Wait until you feel sick. Diagnose the disease. Find a proper remedy. Take the remedy. Wait for it to work. Again, any step might be rate determining. Historically, with what are called serious illnesses, the rate-determining step has been finding a proper remedy. As such remedies are found, once-serious diseases can become even trivial, and the rate-determining step becomes diagnosis or even just waiting for the remedy to work. The goal of curative medicine is to make "feeling sick" the rate-determining step. The goal of preventive medicine is to prevent the entire phenomenon.

4. *Answer*. The net reaction would be: gas + $X \rightarrow$ nothing, which is impossible if we believe in conservation of atoms and mass. Otherwise the mech-

anism fits all the observations and is made acceptable merely by adding "products" to step c. The effect of OH^- is not included.

5. *Hint.* The reactants whose concentrations are used in expressing the rate equation are often those which react in the rate-determining (slow) step. The net reaction is the sum of the mechanistic steps.

Answer. Following the hint we could write the slow step as:

$$(C_6H_{11}O_5)_2O + H^+ \xrightarrow{\text{slow}} (C_6H_{11}O_5)_2OH^+$$

followed, for example, by:

$$(C_6H_{11}O_5)_2OH^+ + H_2O \xrightarrow{\text{fast}} 2\,C_6H_{11}O_5OH + H^+$$

We see that the rate equation describes the assumed slow step. Furthermore, the slow step is between the reactants present in low concentration, and the fast step is between the intermediate and a reactant present in very high concentration, water. Hydrogen ion is regenerated, acting as a catalyst, consistent with its absence in the net equation. Other mechanisms will fit these minimal facts also.

6. *Answer.* Mechanism *A* is not reasonable since the slow step does not involve hydrogen ion or any substance whose concentration is determined by it. Mechanism *B* is reasonable since the slow step involves one of the reactants whose concentration appears in the rate equation and one (H_3O^+) in equilibrium with the other reactant (H^+) listed in the rate equation. Furthermore, the slow step is between substances present in low concentration.

7. *Hint.* Graphical methods are often useful in interpolating data.

Answer. A graph will give a quick answer, especially if we remember that each datum is somewhat uncertain. Or we can simply note in Table 2.2 that the time of debluing always changes more rapidly at higher temperatures. Thus the time will change more rapidly when the temperature drops from 298° to 295° than when it drops the equal interval from 295° to 292°. In this case we have a very quick basis for selecting among the listed answers.

CHAPTER 3

1. *Hint.* How do hydrogen and bromine differ and what factor other than entropy and energy determines reaction rates?

Answer. Besides entropy and energy, the third factor determining reaction rates in our simple picture is collision frequency. When the concentrations and temperatures are the same, the collision frequency is determined by the molecular masses. Thus, at equal temperatures all gases have the same average values of mv^2. Since the Br_2 mass is 80 times that of the H_2 mass, the Br_2 molecules will have a lower velocity by a factor equal to $\sqrt{80} = 9$.

This difference in average molecular velocities accounts for rate differences.

2. *Hint.* Consider the products of the reaction and the probable collisions necessary to convert the reactants into products.

Answer. Both molecules contain identical kinds and numbers of atoms, and the products, CO_2 and H_2O, are identical in each case. Each reaction must proceed by means of collisions between oxygen molecules and gasoline molecules at the high temperatures and pressures inside the engine. The first molecule, which reacts faster, is longer and "leaner." It is the more cylindrical and less spherical of the two. It has a larger surface with which oxygen molecules can collide and cause reaction. The more compact molecule has several "concealed" atoms which clearly cannot collide with oxygen and react until the peripheral atoms have done so. In general, compact molecules will react more slowly than extended ones. Similarly, a length of string dropped into a flame is consumed much more rapidly than the same string first wound into a ball.

3. *Hint.* Since aluminum reacts with most nonmetals, what has probably already happened to the aluminum as it sat in the air?

Answer. Metallic aluminum reacts rapidly with the oxygen in the air but the resulting oxide coat is very adherent and covers the aluminum with a tough layer of oxide which prevents further contact between the metal and oxygen. This oxide reacts only slowly with the bromine, but the products no longer adhere to the surface. Thus, shortly, metallic aluminum is exposed to the bromine and vigorous and rapid reaction begins and continues until either the metal or the bromine is used up.

4. *Hint.* What is produced in chemical reactions besides chemical products?

Answer. Like many chemical reactions, this one is exothermic and the reaction mix becomes hotter and hotter. The rate of reaction increases as the temperature rises and energy is evolved even more rapidly, further increasing both the temperature and the rate. In many reactions the rate can actually become explosive as the temperature gets very high. The problem is to maintain the temperature at a level that will give a reasonable and safe rate. This may be done in a number of ways—e.g., by immersing the reaction vessel in a cooling bath, by introducing cooling coils into the reaction mix, or by allowing the mix to boil and removing the heat in an external condenser which then returns the condensed liquid to the reaction flask. For large-scale, potentially dangerous reactions, a large vat is usually provided into which the reactants can be dumped and quickly cooled if the heat builds up faster than it can be removed by the usual methods.

The change in rate of reaction is often complicated by the action of some of the intermediates or products as catalysts for the over-all reaction. For example, pure HNO_3 is often a slow oxidizing agent, but the presence of HNO_2 (one of the reduction products) catalyzes the action of the HNO_3. In such cases, the reaction temperature must often be lowered more and more as the reaction proceeds to prevent an undesirable increase in rate.

5. *Hint.* K $\propto$ 1/time.

Answer. Plot log (1/t) vs $1/T$. Slope $= -\triangle E^{\ddagger}/4.575$.

CHAPTER 4

1. *Hint.* The more rapidly a person can lose heat to the surrounding, the cooler the person will feel.

Answer. A body warmer than the surrounding atmosphere loses energy to it. This energy goes into making the molecules in the atmosphere move more vigorously. The rate of energy loss depends on the number of molecular collisions with the body per second and the amount of energy transferred in each collision. Since water molecules are lighter than the average molecules in air, they make more collisions per second and hence tend to transmit more energy. Furthermore, water molecules are bent triatomic molecules, in contrast to most of the molecules in air which are linear diatomics. Linear molecules can only rotate in two dimensions and vibrate in one, whereas water can rotate in three and vibrate in three dimensions as well. Thus, each collision with a water molecule can transmit more energy as compared to a collision with a diatomic molecule. The net effect is that gaseous water makes more collisions and absorbs more energy per collision, thus making the body lose (or gain) heat more rapidly than would drier air. (Note that dry air is more cooling if the main mechanism of heat loss is evaporation of perspiration.)

2. *Hint.* Are bond-breaking reactions generally more common at high or at low temperatures?

Answer. At the high temperatures of a rocket nozzle, reactions may not go as much to completion as in a bomb calorimeter at room temperature. Thus, hydrogen and oxygen may not give a 100 per cent yield of water, but rather an appreciable yield of atomic hydrogen and oxygen. Since the atomic hydrogen and oxygen escape from the motor rather than reacting in it with their usual exothermic reaction, less energy is liberated in the motor than anticipated and the temperature is lower than would have been thought. Bond-forming reactions become generally less common and bond-breaking reactions become more common as the temperature rises.

3. *Hint.* Consider one factor at a time and do not worry if you cannot tell with certainty which factor predominates in all circumstances.

Answer. An exact answer requires more data than given but some of the factors can be considered. The factors to be considered are: likelihood of a collision; availability of activation energy (if any is required); likelihood of favorable orientation upon collision (low entropy of activation); strength of the bond formed; and means of getting rid of the energy generated during bond formation. We will not consider relative stabilities of the four

listed products, nor any other reactions than the four listed. Thus the likelihood of the products will be interpreted solely in terms of the likelihood of
these four reactions.

Consider each reactant—H, CH_3, and C_2H_5—separately at first. H is the
lightest in mass, and hence it will make the most collisions. It will collide
equally with all three reactants since all concentrations are the same. Activation energy should be very low (as with all the collisions under consideration) since no bonds need be broken; they have only to be formed. So
we will consider differences here negligible. Atomic hydrogen should have
minimal entropy requirements since it is a spherically symmetrical atom
and, furthermore, is very small. Thus almost every collisional orientation
should be satisfactory as far as the hydrogen is concerned. We see that
hydrogen forms the strongest bond with itself (104 kcal/mole, compared
to 101 and 96 with CH_3 and C_2H_5, respectively). These bond strengths will
have little effect on the reactions being considered, however, but only on
the reverse reactions, which we have agreed not to discuss. Hydrogen will
have the greatest difficulty getting rid of the generated bond energy, since
the energy will almost certainly go into a vibration which will immediately
dissociate the newly formed molecule. The hydrogen is most apt to adhere
to the C_2H_5 since there are in this molecule the most ways of distributing
the added bond energy. Furthermore, the bond energy which must be distributed is a minimum, 96 kcal/mole.

CH_3 will make more collisions than will C_2H_5, (neglecting any size effect)
but fewer than H. Activation energy should be essentially zero as already
discussed. Orientation (entropy) requirements for reaction should be intermediate between H and C_2H_5 with quite appreciable differences between each
of these. Relative bond strengths are not important except in determining the
amount of energy which must be absorbed in the molecule before it flies apart
at the end of one vibration. Table 4.3 lists 83 kcal/mole as the average energy
of the C—C bond, considerably less than those mentioned above for H bonds.
The CH_3 will not be able to absorb this energy as easily as the C_2H_5 (which
has a more complicated atomic arrangement and hence more possible vibrations), but can absorb the energy far better than can the hydrogen atoms.

C_2H_5 has been discussed under the other two. The biggest differences
from H and CH_3 are probably the much higher orientation requirements
and the greater ability to absorb the bond energy generated during a collision.

Conclusions. Very little H_2 will form since a three-body collision is required to get rid of the bond energy. Only a small amount of C_3H_8 will
form, owing to the strict orientation requirements (compared to those of the
hydrogen reactions). Choosing between CH_4 or C_2H_6 as more likely products involves guessing whether the more stringent entropy requirement in
the latter is more than offset by its greater ability to dissipate the generated
bond energy. The answer is probably no. Thus, we might guess that the relative order of yield of these four reactions would be: CH_4, C_2H_6, C_3H_8, and
H_2. Remember that this is not based on equilibrium reasoning, but only on a

simplified approach to the four reactions listed. The equilibrium state will depend on the relative rates of all possible reactions.

4. *Answer.* Aqueous hydrogen ions constitute a concentrated positive electrical field of charge and thus are strongly attracted by the negative ends of polar bonds. The hydrated hydrogen ions can even induce strong polarity in otherwise rather weakly polar bonds. The resulting charge separations usually weaken the original bonds and make them more reactive. Furthermore, the net charge of hydrogen ions can be transferred rapidly through a solution by the sequential transfer of a charged hydrogen atom to a neighboring water molecule which then transfers one of its other hydrogen atoms now bearing the charge to a further water molecule, and so on through the solution. Thus charge is transferred without actual diffusion of particular hydrogen atoms through more than one atomic dimension. In addition, the hydrated hydrogen ion, though constituting a strong positive electrical field, is labile. The proton would as soon be surrounded by water molecules as it would adhere to other polar molecules present. Thus the proton can complete its catalytic chore and then return to be hydrated solely by water molecules without any great energy requirements. Furthermore, the proton is tiny and presents few orientational requirements, such as are found with many other catalysts.

5. *Answer.* Three types of curve are possible depending on whether ΔE is positive, zero, or negative. The difference in potential energy between the reactants and the intermediate molecule (activation energy) is a major factor in determining the rate of the forward reaction. Lowering the potential energy of the products has no effect on the forward rate since the products are not involved in this mechanism. Lowering the potential energy of the intermediate molecule would increase the rate by diminishing the activation-energy requirement for the forward reaction. Diminishing the potential energy of the reactants would decrease the rate by increasing the activation energy for the forward reaction. The potential energies of the various molecules might be lowered experimentally by complexing them. If one of the reactants were ammonia, its potential energy could probably be lowered by adding copper ion to complex with the ammonia. In the same way, the func-

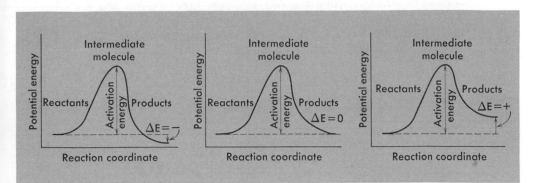

tion of a catalyst is often to lower the potential energy of the intermediate molecule.

CHAPTER 5

1. *Answer.*

　　a. $d(F_2O_2)/dt = k(F_2O_2)$

　　b. $d(H)/dt = d(HBr)/dt = k(H)(HBr)$

　　c. $d(C_6H_5CHO)/dt = k(C_6H_5CHO)^2(CN-)$
　　　 $d(CN-)/dt = O$

2. *Answer.*

　　a. $K = \dfrac{(F_2)(O_2)}{(F_2O_2)}$　　　　　　c. $K = \dfrac{C_6H_5CH(OH)COC_6H_5}{(C_6H_5CHO)^2}$

　　b. $K = \dfrac{(HBr)^2}{(H_2)(Br_2)}$

　　In general there is no direct comparison between the rate equation and the equilibrium-constant expression. Only if the mechanism is very simple will the two expressions contain similar terms. It is very common for the rate expressions to contain concentrations which do not appear in the equilibrium-constant expressions and vice versa.

3. *Answer.* It is impossible to predict which concentrations will cause a change in rate when they are changed. Only experimental data obtained when the iodine and hydrogen ion concentrations are varied, all other factors being kept constant, will give the answer. There is no prior reason why either concentration should or should not be involved. Both the iodine and hydrogen ion concentrations will affect the equilibrium concentrations in a predictable quantitative fashion since both appear in the equilibrium-constant expression

$$K = \frac{(CH_3COCH_2I)(H+)(I-)}{(CH_3COCH_3)(I_2)}$$

4. *Hint.* Remember that the rate equation involves the concentrations of the reactants which are involved in the slowest, or rate-determining, step.

　　Answer. Apparently, from the rate equation, hydrogen ion and acetone, CH_3COCH_3, may collide in the rate-determining step to give an intermediate molecule which then goes on to react to give the final products. The following scheme is consistent with the data presented:

$$CH_3COCH_3 + H^+ \overset{slow}{\rightarrow} CH_3COHCH_3{}^+$$

$$CH_3COHCH_3{}^+ + I_2 \overset{fast}{\rightarrow} CH_3COCH_2I + 2\,H^+ + I^-$$

Other mechanisms are possible.

5. *Answer.* $\Delta E = \Delta E^{\ddagger}_{forward} - \Delta E^{\ddagger}_{reverse}$. The rate of each of the six reactions will increase as the temperature rises, as do all rates. The quantitative effect on the rate can be calculated by using equation 3.12. If ΔE is not zero, the equilibrium concentrations will also be affected by a change in temperature, and in a predictable way. The reaction which has the higher activation energy will increase in rate more with a given rise in temperature. Depending on whether this higher activation energy is associated with the forward or reverse reaction the equilibrium will shift correspondingly. This may be summarized: if ΔE is positive, the equilibrium is shifted to favor products; if ΔE is negative, the equilibrium is shifted to favor reactants. Large values of ΔE mean large shifts in the equilibrium concentrations as the temperature changes.

CHAPTER 6

1. *Hint.* Remember that $\Delta G = \Delta H - T\Delta S$ is the criterion for equilibrium at constant T and P. In this problem it is far more important that you make guesses you can rationally defend than it is to guess the answers given below by mere chance.

Answer. In general, if more bonds break than form, as in parts a and e, ΔH will be positive. If more bonds form than break, ΔH will be negative, as in part b. c, d, f, and g may be difficult to guess on this basis alone; but hydrogen and oxygen are almost always more strongly bonded in H_2O than in other combinations (thus c and d should have negative values of ΔH, and g should have a positive ΔH). The most difficult to evaluate are f and g, since all the substances involved have strong bonds. However, CO_2 is especially stable, so ΔH is probably negative in f. ΔS is usually positive if more molecules, especially gaseous molecules, are present after reaction, since this means greater randomness. Thus ΔS should be positive for a, c, d, e, and g, and should be negative for b and f. ΔH determines the tendency of a reaction to occur at low temperature, where the $T\Delta S$ term is small. Negative values of ΔH mean the reaction tends to occur at low temperatures. Positive values of ΔH mean the reverse reaction tends to occur at low temperatures. Positive values of ΔS mean the reaction tends to occur more at high temperatures. Negative values of ΔS mean the reaction has less tendency to occur at higher temperatures.

We summarize our predictions for the reactions in the following table:

Reaction	ΔH	ΔS	Favored at Lower T	Favored at Higher T
a. $C_2H_5OH_{(g)} = C_2H_{4(g)} + H_2O_{(g)}$	+	+	←	→
b. $Cl_{2(g)} + CO_{(g)} = COCl_{2(g)}$	−	−	→	←
c. $C_3H_{8(g)} + 5\,O_2 = 3\,CO_{2(g)} + 4\,H_2O_{(g)}$	−	+	→	→
d. $NH_4NO_{3(s)} = N_2O_{(g)} + 2\,H_2O_{(g)}$	−	+	→	→
e. $AgCl_{(s)} = Ag^+_{(aq)} + Cl^-_{(aq)}$	+	+	←	→
f. $2\,CO_{(g)} = CO_{2(g)} + C_{(s)}$	−	−	→	←
g. $C_{(s)} + H_2O_{(g)} = CO_{(g)} + H_{2(g)}$	+	+	←	→

2. *Hint.* Remember that $\triangle G = \triangle H - T\triangle S$. Note dimensions of $\triangle H$, S, T, and $\triangle G$. They must be consistent. We will use three significant figures.

Answer.

						$\triangle H_{reaction}$	$\triangle S_{reaction}$	$T\triangle S_{reaction}$	$\triangle G$	Direction at 298°K
a.	SO_2	$+$	$\frac{1}{2}O_2$	$=$	SO_3					
$\triangle H_f$	$-71,000$		0		$-94,500$	$-23,500$	-22.7	-6760	$-16,700$	$\rightarrow$
S	59.4		24.5		61.2					
b.	CO	$+$	H_2O	$=$	CO_2	$+$ H_2				
$\triangle H_f$	$-26,400$		$-57,800$		$-94,100$	0	$-9,900$	-10.0	-2980	$-6,900$	$\rightarrow$
S	47.2		45.1		51.1	31.2				
c.	$2\,H_2$	$+$	O_2	$=$	$2\,H_2O$					
$\triangle H_f$	0		0		$-115,600$	$-115,600$	-21.2	-6310	$-109,300$	$\rightarrow$
S	62.4		49.0		90.2					
d.	H_2	$+$	SO_3	$=$	H_2O	$+$ SO_2				
$\triangle H_f$	0		$-94,500$		$-57,800$	$-71,000$	$-34,300$	12.1	3610	$-37,900$	$\rightarrow$
S	31.2		61.2		45.1	59.4				
e.	H_2	$+$	C_2H_4	$=$	C_2H_6					
$\triangle H_f$	0		$12,600$		$-20,200$	$-32,800$	-28.8	-8590	$-24,200$	$\rightarrow$
S	31.2		52.5		54.9					
f.	$2\,HCl$	$=$	H_2	$+$	Cl_2					
$\triangle H_f$	$11,100$		0		0	$44,100$	-4.8	-1430	$45,500$	$\leftarrow$
S	89.3		31.2		53.3					

When all ingredients are present in equimolar amounts, c is farthest from equilibrium (most negative $\triangle G$) and b is closest. At higher temperatures (assuming $\triangle H$ and $\triangle S$ are unchanged) reaction d would have a greater tendency to occur ($\triangle S$ is positive). All the rest would have less tendency to occur at higher temperatures. Their reverse reactions become more probable.

Index